READ, THINK
and WRITE

READ, THINK
and WRITE

A carefully planned course in comprehension,
vocabulary enlargement and self-expression.

By HAYDN RICHARDS

SCHOFIELD & SIMS LTD.
HUDDERSFIELD

0 7217 0106 X

This edition 1968
Reprinted 1969
Reprinted (Twice) 1970
Reprinted 1971
Reprinted (Twice) 1972
Reprinted 1974
Reprinted 1975
Reprinted (Twice) 1976
Reprinted 1977

Printed in Great Britain by
Henry Garnett & Co. Ltd.,
Rotherham and London
Bound in Scotland

CONTENTS

5

TO THE PUPIL WHO WILL USE THIS BOOK

One of the most important things you can learn during the years you spend at school is how to **understand** what you read.

The purpose of this book is to help you to think about what you read, and by enlarging your vocabulary to encourage you to express yourself fluently in good English.

The extracts chosen are from the world's greatest literature, from books which every child should read with the greatest enjoyment.

Exercise 1

Snow-shoes

Snow-shoes are made of a light, strong framework of wood, varying from three to six feet long by eighteen and twenty inches broad, tapering to a point before and behind, and turning up in front. The framework is filled up with a netting of deerskin threads, which unites lightness with great strength, and permits any snow that may chance to fall upon the netting to pass through it like a sieve.

They are not used like skates, with a sliding, but with a stepping action, and their sole use is to support the wearer on the top of the snow, into which, without them, he would sink up to the waist. This does not mean that they do not break the surface at all, but that the depth to which they sink is trifling, and varies according to the state of the snow and the season of the year. In the woods they sink frequently about six inches, while on frozen rivers, where the snow is packed solid, they sink only two or three inches, and sometimes so little as to render it preferable to walk without them.

With snow-shoes a man can journey over miles of trackless wilderness, over snow so deep that one hour's walk through it without such aids would completely exhaust the stoutest trapper, and advance him only a mile or so on his journey.

(Adapted from *The Fur Traders*, by R. M. Ballantyne.)

1. What is the framework of a snow-shoe made of?
2. What are stretched across this framework?
3. Give two reasons why this material is used.

4. For about how long could a man wearing no snow-shoes walk on soft snow before becoming exhausted?
5. What distance would he probably cover in this time?
6. What difference is there between the action of a man skating on ice and one walking with snow-shoes on soft snow?
7. What is the only purpose for which snow-shoes are worn?
8. What would happen to a person shod with ordinary boots or shoes travelling over soft snow?
9. The depth to which the wearer of snow-shoes sinks varies according to the state of the snow and the time of year.
   (a) Where would he sink to the greatest depth?
   (b) When would he sink to the greatest depth?
10. When would a traveller prefer to walk without snow-shoes?

Word Study

1. The word **snow-shoe** is made up of two words. Each of the missing words in the sentences below begins with **snow**. Complete these sentences, using your dictionary if necessary:
   (a) A ——— is a feathery piece of snow.
   (b) The children were throwing ——— at one another.
   (c) When a town or village is completely shut in by snow it is said to be ———.
   (d) A ——— mountain is one which has its top covered with snow, like Mount Everest.
   (e) A ——— is a bank of snow piled up by the wind.
   (f) The ——— is a small plant with white flowers which blooms in early spring.
   (g) In large towns and cities snow is cleared from the streets by means of ———.

2. A person who traps animals is called a **trapper**. What are the doers of these actions called:
   (a) one who **begs;**
   (b) one who **governs;**
   (c) one who **competes;**
   (d) one who **presides;**
   (e) one who **types;**
   (f) one who **serves?**
3. Write the word in the passage above which means **without any paths**.
4. Which word means **becoming gradually smaller towards one end**?
5. Write a word of five letters which means the same as **frequently**.
6. Give a simple word of four letters which means the same as **sole** in this passage.
7. The word **preferable** means **to be preferred**. What words, all ending with **able**, are indicated by the meanings given below:
   (a) capable of being moved;
   (b) having considerable value;
   (c) liable to perish or decay;
   (d) showing great gain or profit;
   (e) worth wishing for or desiring;
   (f) worthy of respect?
8. There are many kinds of **footwear**. Can you name these:
   (a) heavy boots or shoes with leather uppers and wooden soles worn by gardeners, farm-workers and others doing rough work;
   (b) the deerskin shoes worn by Red Indians;
   (c) a kind of shoe once worn by Roman soldiers, consisting of a sole fastened to the foot by straps. Many children and grown-ups now wear shoes of this type;

11

(d) a shoe, hollowed out of a single piece of wood, once worn by peasants in Holland, France, Belgium and other countries on the Continent;

(e) light indoor shoes which can be slipped on and off easily;

(f) rubber shoes worn over ordinary shoes in very wet weather?

Composition

1. Use the adjectives formed in Question 7 in sentences of your own.
2. Write a brief description of any sport played in the snow.
3. Explain how you would make a snowman.

Exercise 2

A Red Indian Village

The village, at which they soon arrived, was situated in the midst of a most interesting and picturesque scene. Hundreds of tents or "lodges" of buffalo skins covered the ground, and thousands of Indians—men, women and children—moved about the busy scene. Some were sitting in their lodges, lazily smoking their pipes, but these were chiefly old and infirm veterans, for all the young men had gone to the hunt. The women were stooping over their fires, busily preparing maize and meat for their husbands and brothers; while myriads of little brown and naked children romped about everywhere, filling the air with their yells and screams, which were only equalled, if not surpassed, by the yelping dogs that seemed innumerable.

Far as the eye could reach were seen scattered herds of horses. These were tended by little boys who were totally destitute of clothing, who seemed to enjoy the practice of shooting with little bows and arrows. No wonder that these Indians became expert bowmen. There were urchins there, scarce two feet high, who could knock blackbirds off the trees at every shot, and cut the heads off the taller flowers with perfect certainty. There was much need, too, for the greatest skill they could attain, for the very existence of the Indian tribes of the prairies depends on their success in hunting the buffalo.

(Adapted from *The Dog Crusoe*, by R. M. Ballantyne.)

1. What were the Indian tents made of?
2. Who were sitting in the lodges smoking?

3. Why were there no young men in the village?
4. How were the women of the village occupied?
5. What were the children wearing?
6. What made as much noise as the children, if not more?
7. Who looked after the horses?
8. Name two shooting feats performed by the Indian boys.
9. Why was it necessary for the Indians to be skilful with bow and arrow?
10. Name some ways in which the buffalo was useful to the Indians.

Word Study

1. Which word in this passage tells us that the dogs were **too many to be counted**?
2. Write the word in the extract which means **Indian Corn**.
3. The Indian children enjoyed their shooting practice. Complete this proverb:

   Practice makes ———————.

4. Write **one** word which means **destitute of clothing**.
5. A **veteran** is a person experienced in war, or in some trade or profession for many years. Can you give the names of the people described below?
   (a) A very poor person who depends on charity.
   (b) A man who will get somebody's property, wealth or title after the death of the owner.
   (c) One who loves his country and is always loyal to it.
   (d) A person who is entertained at another's house.
   (e) A person who entertains others at his house or elsewhere.
   (f) One who hides in a ship to get a free passage.
   (g) A person who uses his power cruelly or unjustly.

14

(h) A person who flees from his own country to another country for safety.

(i) One who spends most of his time studying and reading.

(j) A person who assumes a false name or character.

6. We are told that the Indians lived in **tents**, or **lodges**. Can you give two words which are the names of Indian dwellings, one beginning with **w** and the other with **t** ?

7. The Indian children could knock blackbirds off the trees at every shot. Write a word beginning with **m** which denotes that a man is a crack shot.

8. Three words here refer to big numbers:

thousands; myriads; hundreds.

Look in your dictionary to see what a myriad is, then write these three words in order, starting with the one which shows the smallest number.

Composition

1. Imagine that you are a visitor to the Indian village described in this extract. Say what would interest you most, and why.

2. Write a brief description of an old Indian chief seated outside his lodge, lazily smoking his pipe.

3. Write a short account of an Indian attack on a party of white men as it might have been told by an old Indian chief to a number of young braves.

Exercise 3

How We Reached the Island

A couple of cocks and two hens were placed in the tubs, and covered over with pieces of wood to keep them from jumping out. I then set free the ducks, geese and pigeons, hoping that they would reach land either through the air or by water.

The tide was flowing as we quitted the wreck, and helped to carry us towards the land. As we glided into the open sea, the two dogs, Turk and Juno, which had been left on the wreck, sprang into the water and swam after us. Both were of large size, so we dared not take them on board, but by now and then resting their forepaws on the planks they managed to follow us without much trouble.

The sea was calm, and slowly but surely we neared the land, so that presently we could see trees which looked like coconut palms.

I now observed a narrow bay, and succeeded in guiding our boat towards the entrance, where the water was just deep enough to float it. With little trouble we reached a low shady bank, and here it was easy for us to land.

The dogs had already arrived, and leaped and barked with joy. The ducks and geese, which also were there, quacked to welcome us, and the cries of the flamingoes that flew away as we appeared, mingling with the screams of the penguins perched on the rocks, made a strange concert.

(Adapted from *The Swiss Family Robinson*, by J. R. Wyss.)

1. Was the tide coming in or going out at the time?

2. Why were the tubs, in which were the cocks and hens, covered over?
3. Use two verbs to describe the two ways in which the ducks, geese and pigeons could reach land.
   They could ――― or they could ――――.
4. Why were the two dogs left on the wreck?
5. How did the dogs rest occasionally when swimming towards land?
6. Was the boat travelling quickly?
7. What did the trees they first saw resemble?
8. Where did the party make for?
9. Did they have much difficulty in landing?
10. Name two kinds of birds which were already on the island before the party left the wreck.

Word Study

1. Which word in the extract means **two**?
2. Write the word of seven letters which means **left**.
3. Which word has the opposite meaning to **failed**?
4. The forepaws of a dog are its **front** paws. Complete the words in these sentences which begin with **fore.**
   (a) The weather **fore**――― says that it will be fine and warm.
   (b) The horse had broken its **fore**――― in the race.
   (c) Your **fore**―――― is the one you usually point with.
   (d) Ernest cut his **fore**――― just above the eye.
   (e) Jack tumbled head **fore**――― into the duckpond.
5. The word **guiding** in the extract begins with **gu**. Can you supply the missing words in these sentences beginning in the same way?
   (a) I tried to **gu**――― Peter's weight, but I was 1 kg out.
   (b) There was a sentry on **gu**――― at the railway bridge.

17

(c) Every good host looks after his **gu** – – –.

(d) The prisoner was found **gu** – – – – and sentenced to life imprisonment.

(e) Mary keeps a **gu** – – – – pig for a pet.

6. Look at these two sentences:

      The dogs **barked** with joy.

      The ducks **quacked** to welcome us.

What noises are made by the following creatures? Use these words in sentences of your own.

lions	wolves ....
horses	cats ....
sheep	elephants ....
donkeys	snakes ....
cows	pigs ....

Remember that some animals make more than one kind of noise; if you can give more than one word, do so.

Composition

Imagine that you were one of the party in this story and that you were writing an account of your experiences in a book which you had rescued from the wreck. How would you describe:

(a) the shipwreck;

(b) the building of the raft;

(c) how land was reached;

(d) life on a desert island?

Exercise 4

Going Down Hill on a Bicycle

With lifted feet, hands still,
I am poised, and down the hill
Dart, with heedful mind;
The air goes by in a wind.

Swifter and yet more swift,
Till the heart, with a mighty lift
Makes the lungs laugh, the throat cry—
"O bird, see; see, bird, I fly!

"Is this, is this your joy,
O bird? Then I, though a boy,
For a golden moment share
Your feathery life in air!"

Say, heart, is there aught like this
In a world that is full of bliss?
'Tis more than skating, bound
Steel-shod to the level ground.

Speed slackens now; I float
Awhile in my airy boat,
Till, when the wheels scarce crawl,
My feet to the pedals fall.

Alas, that the longest hill
Must end in a vale; but still,

Who climbs with toil, wheresoe'er,
Shall find wings waiting there.

Henry Charles Beeching

(From *In a Garden*, by kind permission of John Lane.)

1. Was the cyclist a boy or a girl? How do you know?
2. Write any words or phrases which show that the rider was travelling fast.
3. What sounds does the rider make in travelling downhill?
4. Which line tells us that the rider finds life pleasant?
5. Which does the rider prefer, cycling downhill or skating?
6. Which line shows us that the hill was not a very long one?
7. The rider's feet are off the pedals when he rides downhill. When are they put on the pedals again?
8. Although fond of thrills, the rider is careful. Write the phrase which tells us this.
9. Which sentence shows that the rider was sorry to reach the bottom of the hill?
10. How do we know that the rider considers this ride the most enjoyable thing in the world?

Word Study

1. Write the word in the poem which means **anything**.
2. Give another word for **vale**.
3. Which word means **hard work**?
4. The word ————— means **happiness**.
5. Write the opposite of **swifter**.
6. Write three pairs of words in the poem which rhyme, then add three rhyming words of your own to each pair, like this:

20

float
boat } throat, wrote, note.

7. The verb **slacken** in the poem is formed by adding **en** to the adjective **slack**. The missing words in these sentences are formed in the same way. Write them.
   (a) We put sugar in our tea to ———————— it.
   (b) Tomatoes ————— quickly in hot weather.
   (c) Butchers ———————— their knives when they become blunt.
   (d) Cyclists should ———————— the nuts on their cycles if they become slack.
   (e) Farmers —————— their poultry for the Christmas markets.
   (f) When our lips are dry we ———————— them with our tongues.

8. A person who **cycles** is called a **cyclist**. What are these people called? Each word ends with **ist**.
   (a) one who plays a violin;
   (b) one who extracts teeth;
   (c) a person who sells cigarettes, etc.;
   (d) one who looks on the bright side of life;
   (e) one who looks on the gloomy side of life;
   (f) one who can make his voice appear to come from elsewhere.

9. The adjective **golden** (golden moment) is formed by adding **en** to the noun **gold**. What adjectives ending with **en** are indicated below?
   (a) a garment made of wool (mind your spelling);
   (b) a cross made of wood;
   (c) hair which is the colour of flax;

21

(d) an idol made of brass;

(e) sky the colour of lead;

(f) a material made from silk, or resembling silk.

Vocabulary Quiz

Complete the following sentences:

1. The ————————— of a bicycle prevent the rider being splashed with mud from the wheels.
2. The seat on which a cyclist sits is called the ——————.
3. To stop a bicycle the rider applies the ——————.
4. A cyclist uses a pump to in————— the tyres.
5. The short piece of tubing which connects the pump to the valve of the tube is called a —————————.
6. The centre part of a wheel is called the ———.
7. The steel wires which run from the centre of the wheel to the rim are known as ——————.
8. A bicycle made for two is called a ——————.

Composition

1. Write a composition on "How I Learnt to Ride a Bicycle".
2. Give as many hints as you can on how to keep a bicycle in good running order.
3. Describe briefly how you would mend a puncture.

Exercise 5

A Narrow Escape

In their search for venison the hunting party moved forward till Martin, who was in advance, made a signal to those who followed that the deer were in sight. After a moment or two reconnoitring he informed them that there were twelve or thirteen deer scraping up the snow about a hundred yards ahead. They crept forward; Malachi told each of them which animal to fire at, and they fired nearly simultaneously. Three of the beasts fell, two others were wounded, the rest of the herd bounded off like the wind.

Alfred had fired at a fine buck which stood apart from the rest, and the animal was badly wounded, and Alfred saw it flounder into a thicket. They all ran up to where the dead animals lay, and as soon as they reloaded their rifles Alfred and Martin went on the track of the one which was badly wounded. They had forced their way through the thicket for about fifty yards, guided by the track of the animal, when they started back to the loud growl of some beast.

Alfred saw that a puma had taken possession of the deer and was lying over the carcase. He levelled his rifle and fired; the beast, although badly wounded, immediately sprang at him and seized him by the shoulder. Alfred was sinking under the animal's weight and from the pain he was suffering when Martin came to his rescue and put his rifle ball through the head of the beast, which fell dead.

(Adapted from *The Settlers in Canada*, by Capt. Marryat.)

1. What was the party hunting?
2. Who first saw the deer?
3. Why, do you think, the deer scraped up the snow?
4. Who gave the order to fire?
5. Was this man's plan a wise one?
6. How do you know that the range was less than a hundred yards?
7. How many deer were killed by the party?
8. What happened to the buck which Alfred wounded?
9. What did every member of the party do after firing?
10. What precaution did Alfred and Martin take before looking for the wounded buck?
11. How were they able to find the buck?
12. Was the buck still alive when they found it?
13. What animal gave the loud growl at which they started back?
14. Give two reasons why Alfred sank to the ground.
15. How did Martin save Alfred's life?

Word Study

1. The dead body of an animal is called a **carcase**. What is the dead body of a **human being** called?
2. The hunters saw a **herd** of deer. **Herd** is a collective noun. What collective nouns are used for the following:
   (a) a ————— of fish;
   (b) a ——————— of whales;
   (c) a ———— of wolves;
   (d) a ————— of bees;
   (e) a ——————— of swallows;
   (f) a ————— of sheep?
3. Was the deer at which Alfred fired a male or a female?
4. Which word in this passage means **at the same time**?

24

5. The word **forward,** which has been formed from the two words **fore** and **ward,** refers to **a position in front** of the hunters. Several words can be combined with **ward,** e.g., **inward; outward; westward; upward; downward; windward; leeward; northward; landward; homeward;** etc. Complete each of these sentences by using similar words.

(a) The good ship Sybil was ——————— bound for New York.

(b) Christine is so ———————— in arithmetic that she cannot do simple sums.

(c) I have just finished reading a fine book called "————————Ho!"

(d) The ———————— side of a ship is that on which the wind is blowing.

(e) The sheltered side of a ship is called the ——————— side.

(f) Looking —————— we saw the dark blue sky studded with myriads of twinkling stars.

6. Write **the head of the beast** in three words.

7. Several English words have been formed by placing the letter **a** before certain common words: e.g., **apart** (found in the extract); **aside; away; awake; abreast; astir; afresh; afoot;** etc. Can you find words of this kind to complete the following sentences?

(a) Bob jumped into bed and was soon fast ——————.

(b) We were not allowed to go —————— the Queen Elizabeth II.

(c) The Canadian Pacific Railway runs right —————— Canada.

(d) After three months at sea the sailors were glad to go ——————.

(e) A ship which is behind another is said to be —————— of it.

(f) The intense heat of the sun set the dry grass ——————.

8. **Venison** is the **flesh of a deer**. Say what the flesh of each of these animals is called:
   (a) a sheep;   (c) a cow;
   (b) a pig;   (d) a calf.

Composition

1. Imagine that you are Martin. Describe what happened when you saved Alfred's life.
2. Imagine that you are Alfred, quite a young boy, and that you are telling your parents how Martin came to your rescue. What would you say?

Exercise 6

Cast up by the Sea

Two empty rum casks were firmly lashed parallel together by means of broken oars that formed a framework in which the casks were beautifully secured. On top of the buoyant raft, well secured in the centre between the two casks, was a box covered with a piece of tarpaulin fastened down with nails to keep the contents dry. It was an old wine-case, and as Paul broke off the nail-heads with a stone, and removed the tarpaulin, a few bars of wood beneath that had supported the waterproof cover were easily withdrawn. A rich cashmere shawl was loosely arranged above some object; beneath this was a wrapper of pink flannel. With extreme curiosity Polly removed this covering, and started back with an exclamation of surprise that was echoed by the crowd, as the mystery of the box was suddenly revealed. Apparently asleep or dead lay the body of an infant about two months old, the image of her own boy, but pale as alabaster.

"Is it dead?" asked Polly, trembling with emotion as she regarded the motionless figure that lay before her like an apparition of her own child.

"I fear it is," said Paul, "but I'll carry box and all up to the cottage and we'll see what can be done."

Followed by his wife Paul ascended the zigzag path with his burden and quickly reached his cottage on the cliff. Having placed the box gently on the floor, Polly took away the damp shawl and wrappers; and, covering the child with a warm flannel, she held it close to her breast and briskly rubbed its back and spine. It was very cold, but the limbs were not stiff, so she was hopeful. In a few minutes it gasped faintly, and to her intense delight, after an hour's careful attention she heard it cry lustily. Then she dressed it in some clothes that had belonged to her own child, and felt a mother's happiness as it clung to her breast.

(Adapted from *Cast up by the Sea*, by Sir S. W. Baker.)

1. Describe how the raft had been made.
2. What helped the raft to float so well?
3. What steps had been taken to keep the contents of the box dry?
4. What had the box been used for at one time?
5. How did Paul remove the tarpaulin?
6. Give two reasons why Polly gave an exclamation of surprise when she looked into the box.
7. Where did Paul take the box?
8. What phrase tells us that Paul lived close at hand?
9. How did Paul reach the top of the cliff?
10. How did Polly know that the child was not dead?
11. What did she do to bring it round?
12. How long was it before the child revived?
13. How can you tell, by reading this extract, that Polly's own child had died?
14. Was the rescue of the child witnessed by many people?

Word Study

1. The casks were lashed **parallel** together. Draw two **parallel** straight lines in your book 3 cm long and 1 cm apart.
2. Write the word in this passage which means **ghost**.
3. Paul ascended the cliff in a **zigzag** manner. Draw a **zigzag** line about 5 cm long in your book.

28

4. What is meant by the child's **limbs**?
5. Which word in the extract is opposite in meaning to **concealed**?
6. Which word tells us that the raft floated well?
7. Many words end with **ant**, like **buoyant**. Can you find the words ending in **ant** which will fit the meanings given below?
   (a) empty, like a house which is not occupied;
   (b) sweet-smelling, like a rose;
   (c) brave (word of seven letters beginning with **v**);
   (d) knowing very little or nothing;
   (e) quick to notice; watchful.
8. For what purpose are **tarpaulins** generally used?
9. Give another word for **spine**.
10. Write the word in the extract which contains the prefix **sur**. Give other words beginning with **sur** to complete these sentences.
   (a) The troops refused to **sur**————— to the enemy.
   (b) An island is land completely **sur** ———————— by water.
   (c) To **sur**————— an obstacle is to overcome it.
   (d) The victim of the accident is not expected to **sur**————.
   (e) Experts arrived to **sur**——— the land.

Composition

1. Write an account of this incident in your own words without the use of inverted commas.
2. Relate the conversation which might have taken place between Paul and Polly after the child had been taken to the cottage.
3. We are told that the rescue was witnessed by a crowd of

people. Imagine that one of the onlookers was an old sailor with grey hair and beard, weatherbeaten face and keen, blue eyes; dressed in navy blue serge trousers, a woollen jersey of the same colour, peaked cap and leather sea-boots. Write as full a description of him as you can.

Exercise 7

Aunt Dorothy Grumbit

Aunt Dorothy Grumbit was mild, and gentle, and little, and thin, and old—perhaps seventy-five; but no one knew her age for certain, not even herself. No one knew the extent of her poverty any more than they did her age; but she herself knew it and felt it deeply—never so deeply as when her orphan nephew Martin grew old enough to be put to school and she had not the means to send him. But love is quick-witted and resolute. A residence of six years in Germany had taught her to knit stockings at a rate that cannot be described. She knitted two dozen pairs. The vicar took one dozen, the doctor took the other. The fact soon became known. Shops were not numerous in the village in those days, and the wares they supplied were only second-rate. Orders came pouring in; Mrs. Grumbit's knitting-wires clicked, and her hands wagged with amazing rapidity and regularity; and Martin Rattler was sent to school.

Whilst knitting she sat in a high-backed chair in a very small deep window, through which the sun streamed nearly the whole day, and out of which there was the most charming view, but Mrs. Grumbit never looked at it, for the simple reason that she could not have seen it if she had. Half-way across the parlour was the extent of her natural vision. With her spectacles she could just see the fireplace at the other end of the room, and the portrait of her deceased husband, who had been a sea-captain.

(Adapted from *Martin Rattler,* by R. M. Ballantyne.)

1. When did Mrs. Grumbit feel her poverty most of all?
2. How do you know that Martin had no parents?

3. How was Martin related to Mrs. Grumbit?
4. Where did Mrs. Grumbit learn to knit so skilfully?
5. Who were her first two customers?
6. How many pairs of stockings did each of these customers buy?
7. Give two reasons why orders for stockings came pouring in.
8. Why did Mrs. Grumbit make all these stockings?
9. The old lady sat near a window to do her knitting. In which direction do you think this window faced?
10. How do you know that Mrs. Grumbit was a widow?
11. Although there was a charming view from the window near which she worked, the old lady never even looked at it. Why not?
12. How do you know that the stockings knitted by Mrs. Grumbit were of good quality?

Word Study

1. Which word in the extract means **picture**?
2. Write the opposite of **certain; poverty; natural; quick-witted; numerous**.
3. Give the feminine gender of **nephew**.
4. The adjective **natural** has been formed by adding the suffix **al** to the noun **nature**. Can you fill in the missing adjectives, all ending with **al**, in these sentences? Remember that if the noun ends with **e** the **e** is dropped.
   (a) A ———————— holiday is one for the whole nation.
   (b) A man's conduct is —————— when he behaves like a brute.
   (c) A ———————— gift is made to one particular person.
   (d) A —————————— map is one which is divided into sections for easy handling.

(e) A ————————— mason is one who makes
gravestones, monuments, etc.

Family Tree

Mrs. Grumbit was Martin's **aunt**.

Martin was the old lady's **nephew**.

The old lady's **husband** had been a sea-captain.

Many English nouns express relationship, like those in bold type. How many such words can you pick out in these lines from the well-known poem, *The Pied Piper of Hamelin*?

"Out of the houses the rats came tumbling,
   Great rats, small rats, lean rats, brawny rats,
   Brown rats, black rats, grey rats, tawny rats.
   Grave old plodders, gay young friskers,
       Fathers, mothers, uncles, cousins,
   Cocking tails and pricking whiskers,
       Families by tens and dozens,
   Brothers, sisters, husbands, wives—
   Followed the Piper for their lives."

Here is a family tree which shows three generations. Study it well, then answer the questions below:

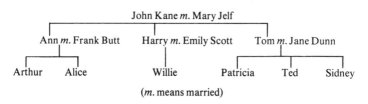

(*m.* means married)

1. How many grandchildren has John Kane?
2. What is Alice's surname?

3. How many boy cousins has Patricia?
4. How many girl cousins has she?
5. What is Willie's surname?
6. How many uncles has Willie?

   Complete these sentences by using nouns which express relationship. Give the correct surname where required.

7. Sidney received a lovely birthday present from his ——————— John Kane.
8. Harry ———— owes his ——————— Tom £5.
9. John Kane is very fond of his ——————— Ann.
10. Willie ———— spent a month's holiday with his ——————— Arthur and Alice.
11. Willie's ————— Frank gave him a warm welcome.
12. Arthur ———— made a stool for his ———— Jane.
13. Harry Kane took his ————— Patricia to the circus.
14. Last week John Kane helped his ——————— Frank Butt with the harvest.
15. Sidney ———— is the ————— of Mr. and Mrs. Frank Butt.
16. Mrs. Mary Kane was delighted when her ——————— Ted passed the Driving Test.
17. Tom Kane sold his ——————————— Frank Butt a car for £400.
18. Tom Kane is exactly the same age as his —————————— Emily.
19. Jane ———— often visits her —————————— John Kane.
20. Mrs. and Mr. John Kane have two ——————————— Emily and Jane.

Exercise 8

Hunting a Gorilla

Presently we caught sight of the gorilla amongst the dense underwood. Peterkin took a steady aim at that part of the creature which was visible and fired, and immediately there burst upon our ears an appalling roar.

For several moments we stood motionless with our guns ready, expecting an immediate attack, and gazing with awe, not unmingled—at least on my part—with fear, at the turmoil of leaves and twigs and broken branches that was going on round the spot where the monster had been wounded.

"Come," said Jack, springing forward, "we must attack him."

We followed close upon his heels, and next moment emerged upon a small, comparatively open space in the midst of which we found the gorilla seated on the ground, tearing up the earth with its hands, grinning horribly, and beating its chest. We saw at once that both its thighs had been broken by Peterkin's shot.

The brute was the most hideous I had ever seen. Apart from its gigantic size it was calculated to strike terror into people's hearts simply by the expression on its face, which was quite satanic.

The instant the brute saw us it tried to spring up, but both its legs gave way, and it collapsed with a growl, biting the earth and twisting and tearing bunches of twigs and leaves in its fury. Suddenly it rushed upon us rapidly by means of its forelegs or arms.

"Look out, Jack!" we cried in alarm.

Jack stood like a rock and deliberately levelled his rifle. Just as the monster approached to within three yards of him he sent a ball into its chest, and the king of the African woods fell dead at our feet.

(Adapted from *The Gorilla Hunters*, R. M. Ballantyne.)

1. Where was the gorilla when the hunters first saw it?
2. Who fired at the gorilla?
3. What made the hunters think that the creature had been hit?
4. Which of the hunters admitted that he felt afraid?
5. What was happening at the spot where the gorilla was wounded?
6. Who led the attack on the wounded gorilla?
7. Name **three** things which the hunters saw the gorilla doing.
8. Where had the gorilla been wounded?
9. Name **two** ways in which the gorilla frightened people.
10. Why could the gorilla not spring up and attack the hunters?
11. In what **three** ways did it show its anger when it collapsed?
12. How was it able to rush at the hunters?
13. Why did the other two hunters warn Jack to look out?
14. How was the gorilla killed?

Word Study

1. The word **satanic** means **like Satan**; **gigantic** means **like a giant**. What words ending with **ic** would you use for:
   (a) a face like that of an angel;
   (b) a person who behaves like an idiot;
   (c) one who shows sympathy towards others;
   (d) a boy who is full of energy;
   (e) a boy who is fit and strong and excels at games?

2. The author calls the gorilla **the king of the African woods**. What is meant by:
   (a) the king of beasts;
   (b) the King of Kings?
3. The hunters stood **motionless**. Can you give words ending with **less** to describe:
   (a) cutlery which does not stain;
   (b) an article which is worth nothing;
   (c) something which has no faults;
   (d) a person who is out of breath;
   (e) a person who is so surprised as to be incapable of speaking?
4. Use the following words in sentences of your own:
   > **emerged; satanic; deliberately; comparatively; dense.**
5. Both the gorilla's **thighs** had been broken by the shot. What parts of the leg are indicated by the following definitions:
   (a) the joint connecting the foot with the leg;
   (b) the front part of the leg below the knee;
   (c) the fleshy part at the back of the leg below the knee;
   (d) the thick part of the leg above the knee?
6. The roar of the gorilla was **appalling**, that is, **terrifying**. Can you describe three **sights** to which this adjective can be applied?
   > e.g., people clinging to a ship which has been torpedoed and is rapidly sinking.

Composition

1. Imagine that you are in Jack's place when the wounded gorilla rushes to the attack. Describe your feelings.

2. From what you have read in this extract and in other books, write a short description of the gorilla.
3. This story is supposed to be told by a boy named Ralph Rover. Write it as it might have been told by his friend Peterkin.

Exercise 9

Colin

By-and-by I began to feel the lack of company, so I resolved to acquire a dog, and bought one from a prospector who was stony-broke and would have sold his soul for a drink.

It was an enormous Boer hunting-dog, a mongrel in whose blood ran mastiff and bulldog and foxhound, and Heaven knows what beside. In colour it was a brindled red, and the hair on its back grew against the lie of the rest of its coat. Someone had told me, or I may have read it, that a back like this meant that a dog would face anything mortal, even to a charging lion, and it was this feature which first caught my fancy.

The price I paid was ten shillings and a pair of boots, which I got at cost price from stock, and the owner departed after warning me to beware of the brute's temper.

Colin, for so I named him, began his career with me by taking the seat out of my breeches and frightening Mr. Wardlaw into a tree. It took me a fortnight to break his vice, and my left arm today bears witness to the struggle. After that he became a second shadow, and woe betide the man who dared raise his hand against Colin's master.

With Colin, I now took to spending some of my ample leisure in exploring and hunting. I had been born with a good eye and a steady hand, and soon became a fine shot with the rifle. I learned how to follow spoor, how to allow for the wind, and stalk under cover. Then, when a shot had crippled the beast we were hunting, Colin was on its track to pull it down. The dog had the nose of a retriever, the speed of a greyhound and the strength of a bull-terrier. I blessed the day when the wandering prospector passed the store.

(From Prester John, by John Buchan. By kind permission
of Thomas Nelson & Sons, Ltd., the publishers.)

1. Why did the writer buy the dog?
2. Why did the owner of the dog sell him?
3. What was the price paid for the dog?
4. What advice was given by the seller to the buyer?
5. Give two examples of the dog's nasty temper.
6. What is meant by the phrase "he became a second shadow"?
7. What did the dog's new master use him for?
8. How do you know that the writer was not a very busy man?
9. Name two characteristics which a good marksman must possess.
10. What was there in the dog's appearance which first attracted the attention of the buyer?
11. Name three things which a hunter must learn.
12. How do you know that the writer was satisfied with his bargain?

Word Study

1. What is a **prospector**?
2. The word **enormous** means **very, very big**. Do you know these words which mean much the same?
    (a) **im** — — — — —

(b) **v––t**

(c) **h––e**

(d) **col–––al**

(e) **gi––––ic**

3. Write the word of five letters which means **abundant**.

4. The word **stalk** here means **to approach a wild animal without being seen**. Can you write a sentence using this word in another sense.

5. Which word refers to the **track** of a wild animal?

6. This passage contains the words:

   betide; beware; became; began.

   Complete the following sentences by using words commencing with **be**.

   (a) Jesus was **be–––––––** by Judas Iscariot.

   (b) To **be–––––––** a person is to make him look small.

   (c) When a person is **be–––––––––** he is confused or puzzled or perplexed.

   (d) The word **be––ow** means **to give**.

   (e) The farmer **bequ––––ed** the farm to his eldest son.

7. What is the opposite of **mortal**?

8. The writer went **exploring** with his dog.

   What are these words beginning with **ex**?

   (a) When you **ex–––––ish** a light you put it out.

   (b) Many artists **ex–––––** their pictures in the National Gallery.

   (c) Pupils who behave badly are sometimes **ex⊥–––ed** from school.

   (d) When you breathe in, your lungs **ex––––**.

   (e) You should never **ex––––** your bare head to the hot sun for any length of time.

9. Use these words (a) **as nouns;** (b) **as verbs**.

   drink; face; fancy; battle; cover; track.

41

Composition

1. Write a composition entitled **A Dog I Bought**.
2. Colin began his career with the writer by taking the seat out of his breeches and frightening Mr. Wardlaw into a tree. Imagine that you witnessed all this. Write a letter to a friend telling him what happened.
3. Write the conversation which might have taken place when the writer was buying the dog from the prospector.

Exercise 10

Buffalo Bill, Pony Express Rider

For three months Billy Cody rode the Pony Express a regular ride of 45 miles, in which he changed to a fresh horse three times.

At one point a short cut in the trail led through a narrow ravine. One day a bearded man jumped quickly into the path and waved a dirty piece of blanket frantically in front of Cody's pony.

The pony, unable to veer from the path because of the steep banks on each side, slid to a stop on its haunches. The bandit held a revolver pointed straight at Billy's heart.

"Reach for the sky, kid," he growled. "Give me the pouches and don't try any tricks."

Billy held up his hands. Freed from his master's steadying touch on the bridle reins the pony tried to spin round in his tracks.

"Grab the bridle, or he'll get away," Billy yelled.

The robber did not stop to think. He stepped forward quickly, left hand extended to grasp the pony's bit.

It was the moment for which Cody was waiting. He fell flat on his horse's neck and his spurs dug deep into the pony's flanks.

The horse lunged forward, knocked the bandit to the ground and trampled on him, his iron-shod feet slashing the man's head and face as he lay upon the ground. He did not rise.

(From *Buffalo Bill,* by Ralph E. Johnston, by kind permission of Allyn and Bacon, Boston.)

43

1. How far did Cody have to ride?
2. How many times did he change horses during a journey?
3. Explain why he changed horses although the journey was not such a very long one.
4. Why did Cody travel through the narrow ravine?
5. Why did the bearded man wave a dirty piece of blanket in front of Billy's horse?
6. Why was the horse unable to turn aside?
7. Say in **two words** what the bandit meant when he said, **"Reach for the sky, kid."**
8. What do you think was in the pouches which the bandit wanted?
9. What did the pony do when Cody held up his hands?
10. Why did Cody ask the bandit to grab the pony's bridle?
11. Name **two things** which Cody did as the bandit stepped forward to grasp the pony's bit.
12. Name **three things** which the pony did to the bandit.

Word Study

1. Complete the unfinished words in these sentences:
   (a) Bill Cody was an expert **horse**———.
   (b) **Horse**———— was used for making beds and for stuffing chairs, etc.
   (c) Rough, boisterous fun is called **horse**————.
   (d) The iron plate nailed to a horse's hoof is called a **horse**————.
   (e) The expression 10 h.p. means 10 **horse**—————.
2. Complete these sentences:
   (a) A male horse is called a ————————.
   (b) A ————— is a female horse.
   (c) A ————— is a young horse.

44

3. This extract contains the names of certain parts of a horse's equipment. What parts are indicated below?
   (a) the metal part which goes into the horse's mouth;
   (b) the leather straps by which the rider guides the horse;
   (c) the leather seat on which the rider sits;
   (d) the supports for the horseman's feet, hung from the seat.

4. A **bandit** is a man who robs people. The criminals mentioned below all rob people. Can you name them?
   (a) a man who steals things from people's pockets;
   (b) one who attacks and robs ships at sea;
   (c) a person who breaks into a house to steal;
   (d) a man on horseback who robs travellers on the public road;
   (e) a person who gets money from people by threatening to reveal something bad about them;
   (f) a person who imitates another person's name on a cheque so that he can draw the money himself.

5. What are the missing words in these well known sayings about horses?
   (a) To ride the ———— **horse** means to be proud and haughty.
   (b) A ———— **horse** is a person who does not show what he can really do until a favourable opportunity presents itself.
   (c) To put the ———— before the **horse** means to reverse the correct order of things, like a boy parting his hair before washing his face.

Composition

1. Write this story of Billy Cody in your own words.

2. Write a composition entitled "A Day in My Life" (by a Pony Express rider).
3. Write a short composition describing some of the many ways in which horses serve mankind, e.g., on the farm, on police duty, especially with the Royal Canadian Mounted Police, on a cattle ranch, etc.

Exercise 11

Tossed in a Blanket

The room was a great big one with a dozen beds, but not a boy that Tom and East could see. Suddenly, in rushed several fifth-form boys looking for youngsters to toss in a blanket. Tom and East at once volunteered to undergo this ordeal, and the procession went down to Number 7, the largest room, and the scene of the tossing, in the middle of which was a great open space. Here they joined other parties of big boys, each with a captive or two, some willing to be tossed, some sullen and some frightened to death.

Then a dozen boys seized hold of a blanket dragged from one of the beds. "In with Scud, quick, there's no time to lose." East was chucked into the blanket. "Once, twice, thrice, and away!" Up he went like a shuttlecock, but not quite up to the ceiling.

"Now, boys, with a will," cried Walker, "once, twice, thrice, and away!" This time he went clean up, and kept himself from touching the ceiling with his hand, and so again a third time, when he was turned out, and up went another boy. And then came Tom's turn. He lay quite still by East's advice, and didn't dislike the "once, twice, thrice," but the "away" wasn't so pleasant. They were in good wind now, and sent him up to the ceiling first time, against which his knees came rather sharply. But the moment's pause before descending was the rub, the feeling of utter helplessness and of leaving his whole inside behind him sticking to the ceiling. Tom was very near shouting to be set down when he found himself back in the blanket, but thought of East, and didn't; and so took his three tosses without a kick or a cry, and was called a young trump for his pains.

(Adapted from *Tom Brown's Schooldays*, by Thomas Hughes.)

1. How many boys are named in this extract?
2. How many of the boys named were tossed?
3. How many times was each boy tossed?
4. How did East keep himself from touching the ceiling?
5. What advice did East give Tom?
6. Write down East's nickname.
7. How did Tom feel during the pause before descending?
8. Why didn't Tom shout to be set down, although he was tempted to do so?
9. Why, do you think, was room Number 7 chosen for tossing?
10. There were three types of captive; name them.
11. Why did the bigger boys call Tom a "trump"?
12. Where did the big boys get the blanket for the tossing?

Word Study

1. This passage mentions a **room with a dozen beds in it**. What is such a room called? What are the following **rooms** called?
   (a) A cool room where milk and cream are kept, and made into butter.
   (b) A room where clerks work.
   (c) The small room in a house where dishes are washed.
   (d) The room in a church where the choir put on their robes.
   (e) A room in which a large collection of books is kept.
   (f) A room for passengers on board ship.
   (g) A room just below the roof of a house.
2. When the author says that the bigger boys were in **good wind** he means that they were in splendid form. All the following sentences contain a word beginning with **wind**. Can you find them?

(a) Years ago **wind** ————— were commonly used for grinding corn.

(b) The air you breathe goes down your **wind** ————.

(c) The **wind** —————— of the car was smashed in the collision.

(d) A **wind** ———— is an unexpected piece of good luck, like receiving a £1 note from a rich uncle, when you are wondering how to get enough to go to the cinema.

(e) The **wind** ———— side of a ship is the side on which the wind is blowing.

(f) The sailing vessels of long ago were called **wind-————————**.

3. A **captive** is a person who is **captured**. What do we call the one who **captures** him?

4. We are told that Tom disliked the feeling of utter **helplessness**. The word **helplessness** is made by adding first **less**, then **ness**, to the *noun* **help**.

Adding **less** to the noun **help** makes the *adjective* **helpless**.

Adding **ness** to the adjective **helpless** makes the *noun* **helplessness**. Now form *adjectives* and *nouns* from the following words in the same way:

Noun	Adjective	Noun
help	helpless	helplessness
hope	....	....
care	....	....
rest	....	....
breath	....	....

5. A **shuttlecock** is a piece of cork with feathers stuck in one end and is used in a game called battledore and shuttlecock, the battledore being a kind of small bat or racket.

In what games are the following used:

(a) a cue;

(b) a racket;

49

(c) a tee;
(d) a joker;
(e) a small white or black ball called the jack?

Composition

1. Write in your own words an account of the tossing of either Tom Brown or East.
2. Imagine that you have been tossed in a blanket. Write a letter to a boy of your own age telling him what it was like.

Exercise 12

The King's Forester

Jacob had never seen Parliamentary troops, for they had not been sent into that part of the country, but their iron skull-caps and dark clothes told him that such these must be, so different were they from the gaily-equipped Cavalier cavalry commanded by Prince Rupert. At the time they advanced, Jacob had been lying down in the fern near some low blackthorn bushes; not wishing to be perceived by them he drew back between the bushes, intending to remain concealed until they should gallop out of sight; for Jacob thought, "I am a King's forester, and they may regard me as an enemy, and who knows how I may be treated by them?" But Jacob was disappointed in his expectation of the troops riding past him, for as soon as they arrived at an oak-tree within twenty yards of where he was concealed, the order was given to halt and dismount.

Jacob learnt from the talk of the troopers that Arnwood was to be burnt down that night, on the suspicion that it was sheltering King Charles, and thanking God for having allowed him to hear the information he hastened on his way. He had been about eight miles from Arnwood when he had hidden himself in the fern. Jacob first went to his cottage to deposit his gun, then saddled his forest pony and set off for Arnwood. In less than two hours the old man was at the door of the mansion; it was then about three o'clock in the afternoon, and being the month of November there was not so much as two hours of daylight remaining.

(Adapted from *Children of the New Forest*, by Capt. Marryat.)

1. Why had Jacob never seen Parliamentary troops before?
2. How did he know that they were Parliamentary troops?
3. What was Jacob doing when the soldiers advanced?
4. Why did he not wish to be seen by the soldiers?
5. What did he expect the soldiers to do?
6. In what way was he disappointed?
7. Name two things which the soldiers were ordered to do when they arrived at the oak tree.
8. How far from Jacob was this tree?
9. How far away was Arnwood?
10. Why was Arnwood to be burnt down that night?
11. Although Jacob wanted the soldiers to gallop out of sight he was afterwards very glad that they had not done so. Why?
12. What did Jacob do on reaching his cottage?
13. About what time was it when Jacob left his cottage?
14. At what time did he arrive at Arnwood?
15. Was he in time to warn the occupants that Arnwood was to be burnt? How do you know?
16. How did the Cavaliers differ from the Parliamentary troops?

Word Study

1. The adjective **Parliamentary** is formed by adding the suffix **ary** to the noun **Parliament**. Add **ary** to the nouns below, then use each of the adjectives so formed in a sentence of your own.

   moment; custom; compliment; second.
2. Write the opposites of:

   advanced; concealed; hastened; different.
3. Write simpler words for:

   perceived; concealed; hastened.

4. Which word in this passage means **horse soldiers**?

5. The word **concealed** occurs twice in this extract. Can you find the words beginning with **con** which will fit into these sentences?
   (a) The prisoner **con**— — — — — to the crime.
   (b) As he had had the pain for several days Mr. Jameson **con**— — — — — his doctor.
   (c) The orchestra was **con**— — — — — by Sir Malcolm Sargent.
   (d) Ten houses were **con**— — — — — — — in the village last year.
   (e) The parents **con**— — — — — to the marriage of their daughter.

6. Jacob lay hidden near some **blackthorn** bushes. Complete these sentences:
   (a) The **black**— — — — — is the fruit of the bramble.
   (b) A man who would steal money from a child is a **black**— — — — —.
   (c) Turning off all the lights in a theatre or town is known as a **black**— — —.
   (d) A man who keeps on working whilst his mates are out on strike is called a **black**— — —.
   (e) The **black**— — — — — was placed on an easel.

7. Write **two** words which mean the same as **not so much as**.

8. There was not so much as two hours of **daylight** remaining. Each of the unfinished words in these sentences contains the word **light**; what are they?
   (a) A — — — — — —**light** can throw a powerful beam of light in any direction, and is used for spotting aircraft at night.
   (b) A — — — — —**light** is a light which burns all night in a child's bedroom.
   (c) A — — — — —**light** is used to illuminate the fronts of buildings.
   (d) A — — — —**light** is a strong light thrown on one particular

53

place or person; sometimes used in a theatre.

(e) When we say that a person is in the ————**light** we mean that he is the centre of public attention and interest.

Composition

1. Write the conversation which might have taken place among the troopers when Jacob overheard their secret.
2. Write a composition entitled "A Secret I Overheard".
3. Describe the scene at any burning building you may have seen.

Exercise 13

Nelson and the Bear

One night, during the mid-watch, young Nelson stole from the ship with one of his comrades, taking advantage of a rising fog, and set off over the ice in pursuit of a bear. It was not long before they were missed. The fog thickened, and Captain Lutwidge and his officers became exceedingly alarmed for their safety. Between three and four in the morning the weather cleared, and the two adventurers were seen, at a considerable distance from the ship, attacking a huge bear. The signal for them to return was immediately made; Nelson's comrade called upon him to obey it, but in vain; his musket misfired, their ammunition was finished, and a chasm in the ice, which divided him from the bear, probably preserved his life. "Never mind," he cried, "just let me get a blow at this devil with the butt of my musket and we shall have him."

Capt. Lutwidge, seeing his danger, fired a gun, which had the desired effect of frightening the beast; and the boy then returned, somewhat afraid of the consequences of his conduct. The captain scolded him for behaviour so unworthy of the office which he filled, and desired to know what motive he could have for hunting a bear.

"Sir," said he, pouting his lip, "I wished to kill the bear so that I might carry the skin to my father."

(Adapted from Robert Southey's *Life of Nelson*.)

1. Why did Nelson and his companion leave the ship?
2. When did they leave the ship? Say roughly between what hours.

3. What helped them to get away without being seen?
4. What effect did the fog have on the captain of the ship?
5. Did the fog last very long?
6. What were the boys seen doing when the fog lifted?
7. Why did Nelson disobey the signal to return?
8. Why did the captain fire the gun?
9. Was Nelson afraid of being punished for his disobedience?
10. What happened when Nelson returned to the ship?
11. Why did Nelson wish to kill the bear?
12. Why did Nelson not shoot the bear, although armed with a musket and within easy range?

Word Study

1. Nelson's musket had **misfired**. The prefix **mis** placed before a verb means **badly, wrongly, improperly**. Can you find these words which begin with **mis**?
   (a) If you have **mis**———— something you have put it in the wrong place and cannot find it.
   (b) To **mis**————— a word is to spell it wrongly.
   (c) To **mis**———— a person is to lead him in the wrong way.
   (d) A person has been **mis**———————— when he has been given wrong information.
   The prefix **mis** may also be used with nouns.
   (e) A suit or costume which fits badly is said to be a **mis**———.
   (f) Another word for **mis**———————is ill-luck.
   (g) Wicked deeds are sometimes called **mis**—————.
   (h) A mistake in printing is called a **mis**—————. A local paper once said that the vicar of the parish was the village's greatest **fiend**. What did the paper mean?
2. The man in charge of a ship is the **Captain**. Who are in charge of the following:

(a) a boys' school;

(b) a railway station;

(c) a bank;

(d) a lighthouse;

(e) a hospital or infirmary;

(f) a post office;

(g) a college or university;

(h) a library;

(i) a railway train;

(j) a group of workers, or some part of a factory?

3. Explain clearly what a **chasm** is.

4. The letters **ch** in **chasm** are sounded as **k**.
   Can you provide a word of this type for each of the following meanings:
   (a) a group of singers;
   (b) a shiny metal used for plating other metals, much used on bicycles and cars;
   (c) something given to people about to undergo an operation in order to prevent them feeling pain;
   (d) the form of an insect when it is in a case; a butterfly has this form after it has been a caterpillar;
   (e) a round flower with many petals which was brought to this country from Japan?

5. Nelson and his friend left the ship during the mid-watch. The missing words in these sentences begin with **mid**. Complete the sentences.
   (a) Another word for noon is **mid** – – –.
   (b) Cinderella was told not to stay at the ball after **mid** – – – – –.
   (c) The central vein of a leaf is called the **mid** – – –.
   (d) The time around June 21st is called **mid** – – – – – –.
   (e) The centre part of a river is called **mid** – – – – – –.

Composition

1. Imagine that you are Nelson, writing an account of this adventure in a letter to your parents. What would you say?
2. Write the actual words which the captain of the ship might have said:
   (a) in scolding Nelson for his misconduct;
   (b) in asking him why he had risked his life.

Exercise 14

Hunted by Bloodhounds

We struggled up the gorge that led to the precipice; and the next moment we reached a level platform covered with tufted grass, where we stood for some moments gathering breath and nerving ourselves for the desperate struggle. I could not help looking over the precipice. It was a fearful sight. In a vertical line, two hundred feet below, the stream rushed through the canyon, broke upon a bed of sharp, jagged rocks, and then glided on in seething snow-white foam. There was no object between the eye and the water, not even a tree to break the fall.

It was some minutes before our unnatural enemies made their appearance, but every howl sounded nearer and nearer. Our trail was warm, and we knew they were scenting it on the run. At length the bushes crackled, and we could see white breasts gleaming through the leaves. A few more springs and the foremost bloodhound bounded out upon the bank, and throwing up his broad jaw uttered a hideous growl.

He was at fault where we had entered the water. His comrades now dashed out of the thicket and joined in a chorus of disappointment, but an old dog, scarred and cunning, kept along the bank until he reached the top of the canyon where we had made our crossing. Here the hound entered the channel, and springing from rock to rock reached the point where we had dragged ourselves out of the water. A short yelp announced to his comrades that he had found the scent, and they all threw up their noses and galloped down.

There was a swift current between two large boulders, and

we had leaped this. The old dog prepared to spring after us when Lincoln fired and the hound dropped in head first and was carried off like a flash.

(Adapted from *The Rifle Rangers*, by Capt. Mayne Reid.)

1. Name two things which the hunted men did on the level ground which they had reached.
2. How did they reach the precipice?
3. How far below them was the stream?
4. What change did the ragged rocks effect in the stream which broke over them?
5. How do you know that at first the bloodhounds had no difficulty in following the trail?
6. Where was the scent lost?
7. How was the cunning old dog able to pick up the scent again?
8. In what way did he tell the other dogs that he had found the scent again?
9. What did the other dogs do when they knew that the scent had been found again?
10. What happened to the old bloodhound as he prepared to spring to the attack?
11. What is meant by the phrase "our unnatural enemies"?
12. Can you tell why the men entered the water?

Word Study

1. This extract contains the names of various **noises** made by dogs:

    e.g., **howl; growl; yelp**.

    Here are some similar words; find the meaning of each word, then use it in a sentence of your own.

    snarl; whimper; whine; bark.

60

2. The **bloodhound** is still occasionally used by the police for tracking criminals.
   (a) What dogs are used in our country for track racing?
   (b) What breed of dog was used for rescuing travellers lost in the snow on the Alps?
   (c) What is England's national dog, John Bull's constant companion?
   (d) Which dog most resembles a wolf?
   (e) What is the name of Germany's national dog, the one with a very long body and extremely short legs?
3. The word **scent** has a silent letter, the **c**. Do you know these words which begin with **sc** sounded as **s**:
   (a) something seen on the stage of a theatre;
   (b) what you would use for cutting paper;
   (c) the rod which the Queen sometimes holds in her hand as a symbol of her power;
   (d) a subject taught in school, about solids, liquids and gases?
4. Write the words in this passage which mean:
   (a) **large rocks rounded or worn by the action of water;**
   (b) **bubbling and foaming;**
   (c) **standing up straight;**
   (d) **a deep narrow valley, usually steep and rocky;**
   (e) **with sharp points sticking out.**
5. Use the following words (a) **as nouns**; (b) **as verbs**.
   object; water; break; spring; flash; point.

Composition

1. Write an account of the shooting of the foremost bloodhound as it might have been told by Lincoln.

2. Write a short account of how an escaped convict was traced by police bloodhounds.
3. Imagine that you have been trespassing in Farmer Brown's orchard, and that you have been chased by his bulldog and taken refuge in a tree. Describe your adventures.

Exercise 15

The Wreck of the White Ship

When at last the *White Ship* shot out of the harbour of Barfleur there was not a sober seaman on board. But the sails were all set, and the oars going merrily. Fitz-Stephen had the helm. The gay young nobles and the beautiful ladies, wrapped in mantles of various bright colours to protect them from the cold, talked, laughed and sang. The Prince encouraged the fifty sailors to row harder yet, for the honour of the *White Ship*. Crash! A terrific cry broke from three hundred hearts. It was the cry the people in the distant vessels of the King heard faintly on the water. The *White Ship* had struck upon a rock—was filling, going down! Fitz-Stephen hurried the Prince into a boat with a few nobles. "Push off," he whispered, "and row to the land. It is not far, and the sea is smooth. The rest of us must die."

But as they rowed away from the sinking ship the Prince heard the voice of his sister Marie, the Countess of Perche, calling for help. He cried in an agony, "Row back at any risk! I cannot bear to leave her!"

They rowed back. As the Prince held out his arms to catch his sister, such numbers leaped in that the boat was overset. And in the same instant the *White Ship* went down.

(From *A Child's History of England*, by Charles Dickens.)

True-False Comprehension Test

Read the above passage through carefully. Then write the

numbers 1 to 10 in a column in your exercise book. Study the statements which appear below. If you think a statement is *TRUE* write T opposite its number; if you consider it *FALSE* write F.

You will get a mark for every correct answer, but a mark will be deducted from your total for every wrong answer. Thus, if you get 8 right and 2 wrong your final score will be 6.

1. Several of the crew of the *White Ship* were drunk.
2. The weather was quite warm when the ship left harbour.
3. The Countess of Perche was a very close friend of the Prince.
4. The ship was travelling at a good speed.
5. The passengers were in high spirits.
6. The *White Ship* was carried onto the rock by the rough sea.
7. The Prince was steering the ship when she struck.
8. The King's ships were a long way from the *White Ship*.
9. The Prince thought only of his own safety.
10. The ship was wrecked quite near the shore.

Word Study

The word **helm** appears in this extract. This is the handle or wheel by which a ship is steered. Do you know what these parts of a ship are called?

1. The forward part of a ship or boat.
2. The hind part of a ship or boat.
3. The main body of a ship, apart from masts, sails, etc.
4. The right-hand side of a ship, looking forward.
5. The left-hand side of a ship, looking forward.
6. The ropes and chains used to support the masts and to work the sails.
7. A round opening in a ship's side to let in light and air.

8. The huge shaped piece of iron, fastened to a rope or chain, which grips the sea bottom and so prevents the ship from drifting.

9. The hinged flat piece of wood or metal at the rear end of a vessel by which it is steered.

10. The revolving shaft with blades which drives a ship through the water.

The *White Ship* was a sailing ship; the boat which was swamped was a rowing boat. Can you name these vessels?

1. The light boats used by Red Indians and propelled by paddles.

2. The light boats, consisting of a wooden framework covered with skins, which were used by the Ancient Britons.

3. The light Eskimo boat used for one person.

4. A vessel which travels under the sea.

5. A ship which carries cargoes of coal.

6. A ship specially built for catching whales.

7. A long, narrow boat used on the canals of Venice.

8. The big passenger ships which make voyages to America and other countries, like the *Queen Elizabeth II*.

9. A ship which goes to almost any country with almost any kind of cargo.

10. A flat-bottomed boat used on rivers and driven along by thrusting a long pole against the river bed.

Exercise 16

David Copperfield Sells His Waistcoat

It was by this time dark; I heard the clocks strike ten as I sat resting. But it was a summer night, fortunately, and fine weather. When I had recovered my breath, and had got rid of a stifling sensation in my throat, I rose up and went on. In the midst of my distress I had no notion of going back.

I was possessed of only three-halfpence in the world, and began to picture myself as a scrap of newspaper intelligence, my being found dead in a day or two, under some hedge; and I trudged on miserably, though as fast as I could, until I happened to pass a little shop where it was written up that ladies' and gentlemen's wardrobes were bought, and that the best price was given for rags, bones and kitchen-stuff.

The master of the shop was sitting at the door in his shirt-sleeves, smoking; and as there were a great many coats and pairs of trousers dangling from the low ceiling, and only two feeble candles burning inside to show what they were, I fancied that he looked like a man of revengeful disposition, who had hung all his enemies, and was enjoying himself.

I went up the next by-street, took off my waistcoat, and came back to the shop-door. "If you please, sir," I said, "I am to sell this for a fair price."

He took the waistcoat, stood his pipe on its head against the door-post, went into the shop, followed by me, snuffed the two candles with his fingers, spread the waistcoat on the counter, and looked at it there, held it up against the light, and looked at it there, and ultimately agreed to give me ninepence for it.

(Adapted from *David Copperfield*, by Charles Dickens.)

1. What time of day was it?
2. What time of year was it?
3. What is there in this extract to show that David had been hurrying and was tired?
4. David was afraid of being found dead under a hedge in a day or two. Why did he think this was likely to happen?
5. What did the notice outside the little shop tell David?
6. Name some other things which the master of the shop bought in addition to second-hand clothes.
7. Where was the master of the shop when David first saw him?
8. What dangled from the low ceiling of the shop?
9. What did David fancy they were?
10. How was the inside of the shop lighted?
11. Why did David go up the next by-street?
12. Who entered the shop first?
13. Name two ways in which the master of the shop examined the waistcoat.
14. How much money did David have altogether when he left the shop?

Word Study

1. Write the words in this passage which mean:
   (a) **luckily;**   (c) **finally;**
   (b) **news; information;**   (d) **put out; extinguished.**
2. The word **newspaper** is made up of the two words **news** and **paper.** The following words begin with **news.** What are they?
   (a) a boy who sells newspapers on the streets, or delivers them to our houses;
   (b) a man who sells newspapers from a shop or a stall;

(c) the paper used in printing newspapers;

(d) the films of current events shown at cinemas.

3. Two words here contain the prefix **dis**:

distress; disposition.

Complete these sentences by using words which begin with **dis**.

(a) The loss of the battleship was a terrible **dis**－－－－－.

(b) The firm allowed me a **dis**－－－－－ of 10p in the £ for prompt payment.

(c) Eczema is a common skin **dis**－－－－.

(d) The behaviour of the ill-mannered mob filled everybody with **dis**－－－－.

4. David **trudged** along the road, that is, he walked wearily and with much effort. Below you will find ten words which describe various ways of walking. These are followed by ten definitions. Can you match the words and the meanings?

> **toddle;   stroll;   swagger;   plod;**
> **march;   stride;   pace;   strut;**
> **limp;   stagger.**

(a) to walk quietly, for pleasure:

(b) to walk proudly and vainly like a peacock:

(c) to walk as soldiers do, to the same time, with steps of the same length:

(d) to walk with very long steps, like a person in a great hurry:

(e) to walk like a drunken man:

(f) to walk with regular steps like a tiger in a cage:

(g) to walk slowly or heavily, like a workman returning home from work after a hard day:

(h) to walk with uneven steps, as a lame person does:

(i) to walk with short, unsteady steps, as a baby does:

(j) to walk with a bold, rude, insolent air of superiority.

Composition

1. Write a brief description of any second-hand clothes shop you have seen.
2. Imagine that you were in David's place. What would you have done with the money obtained by selling the waistcoat?
3. Suppose that you were walking from London to Dover with only three-halfpence in your pocket, as David was doing. Write an account of any one day's happenings, e.g., how you begged at a farmhouse for food and shelter, how you sang for pennies in a village, etc.

Exercise 17

Attacked by Savages

The savages gave a tremendous yell, and as they advanced a dozen spears were thrown at Mr. Ready with so true an aim that, had he not instantly dodged behind the stockade, he must have been killed.

Mr. Seagrave, who had agreed to be stationed at the corner so that he might see if the savages went round to the other side, fired his musket, and the tall chief fell to the ground.

Ready and William also fired, and two more of the savages were seen to drop, amidst the yells of their companions. Juno handed up the other muskets which were ready loaded, and took those discharged, and Mrs. Seagrave, having desired Caroline to take care of her little brother, and Tommy to be quiet and good, came out, turned the key of the door upon them, and hastened to assist Juno in reloading the muskets.

The spears now rushed through the air, and it was well that they could fire from the stockade without exposing their persons, or they would have had but little chance. The yells increased, and the savages now began to attack on every quarter; the most active, who climbed like cats, actually succeeded in gaining the top of the palisade, but as soon as their heads appeared above they were fired at with so true an aim that they dropped down dead outside.

This combat lasted for more than an hour, when the savages, having lost a great many men, drew off from the assault, and the parties within the stockade had time to breathe.

(Adapted from *Masterman Ready*, by Capt. Marryat.)

1. What did Mr. Ready do when the savages threw spears at him?
2. Where was Mr. Seagrave stationed?
3. Why was he stationed in this particular place?
4. What did Mr. Seagrave do when the savages made their attack?
5. What effect did this have on the savages?
6. What part did Juno play in this action?
7. Who helped her in her task?
8. Where were Caroline and Tommy during the attack?
9. What big advantage did the defenders have?
10. Which of the savages reached the top of the palisade?
11. What happened to them when their heads appeared over the top?
12. How do you know that the defenders were crack shots?
13. Why did the savages break off the attack?
14. How long did the attack last?

Word Study

1. Write **two** different words which mean:
   a fence of stakes set firmly in the ground as a defence round a building.
2. What are the opposites of:
   increased; advanced; attack; succeeded?
3. Which words in this extract mean:
   (a) **immediately;**   (d) **battle, or fight;**
   (b) **fired;**   (e) **attack?**
   (c) **uncovering;**
4. The savages flung **spears**; the defenders fired their **muskets**. These are called **weapons**. Give **one** word for each of the following groups. The first is done for you.
   (a) spring; summer; autumn; winter (**seasons**)

(b) hammer; chisel; plane; pincers;

(c) knives; forks; spoons; scissors;

(d) geese; turkeys; ducks; chickens;

(e) wasps; flies; moths; bees;

(f) plates; cups; saucers; basins;

(g) bangles; rings; bracelets; brooches;

(h) boots; shoes; clogs; sandals;

(i) wheat; barley; maize; oats;

(j) cars; lorries; vans; buses.

5. Can you name these **weapons**:
   (a) the war-axe used by Red Indians;
   (b) the short spear with a rope attached which is used for catching whales;
   (c) the club carried by a policeman;
   (d) the blade attached to the barrel of a soldier's rifle;
   (e) the curved piece of wood, used by Australian natives, which returns to the thrower if the target is missed?

6. Juno and her mother **reloaded** the muskets: that is, they loaded them **again**.

   What are these words which begin with **re**:
   (a) to appear again;
   (b) to capture again;
   (c) to make fresh again;
   (d) to write all over again;
   (e) to unite again, to bring together again?

   Use each of the words you have made in a sentence of your own.

Composition

1. Write this story as it might have been told by:
   (a) Mr. Ready;
   (b) Mrs. Seagrave;
   (c) Juno.

2. Write an account of any incident in which a native figures, e.g., Robinson Crusoe's meeting with Friday.
3. Describe the scene in the native village when the defeated warriors returned with their dead and wounded.

Exercise 18

The Big Hunt

The harvest of meat was considered almost as important as that of corn; therefore, while a portion of the men and the whole of the women were engaged in the cultivation of their fields, those who were most active and courageous formed bands of hunters, and provided a supply of flesh. To be distinguished for exploits in the hunt was considered to be more meritorious than to do deeds of valour on the field of battle, and Ned was expected to perform wonders in the chase of wild animals. Next to the king he was the greatest man in the country, as his supposed magic had given him an extraordinary influence.

It was not long before Ned was requested by the king to foretell the result of a hunting expedition that was about to start. Ned declared that great success would attend the hunting party should he and Tim accompany the hunters, so it was arranged that he should take command.

At daybreak on the following morning, Ned, accompanied by Tim and Nero with fifty picked men, started off in five large canoes.

Owing to Ned's prowess with the gun the expedition was very successful. On the return of the hunters crowds of people assembled on the shore to welcome them. Hardly had the canoes touched the sandy beach than they were dragged in triumph to the land. The cargo of meat was discharged with great rapidity, and was transported to the village, where Ned was quickly brought into the presence of the king, who received him with great courtesy, while the principal man gave an account of the expedition.

(Adapted from *Cast up by the Sea,* by Sir S. W. Baker.)

1. Which was considered the more important, meat or corn?
2. Who were chiefly engaged in working in the fields?
3. Did any of the women take part in the hunt?
4. What two qualities was every hunter expected to possess?
5. Why was Ned expected to do wonders in the hunt?
6. What had helped Ned to become the second greatest man in the country?
7. Ned prophesied that the expedition would be successful. In what way did he help to make this prophecy come true?
8. How many hunters were there in the party altogether?
9. How did they travel?
10. Why was the expedition so successful?
11. What was done with the animals which were killed?
12. What kind of reception did Ned get from the king?

Word Study

1. Write **one** word for **cultivation of the fields**.
2. What is a man skilled in magic called?
3. Can you give **one** word for **chase of wild animals**?
4. Write a simple word which means the same as **principal**.
5. Write words opposite in meaning to:
     important; courageous; success.
6. Which word in this extract refers to the **load of goods carried by a ship or boat or canoe**?
7. Find out the meaning of the following words and use each in a sentence of your own:
     distinguished; exploits; assembled; expedition.
8. Write a word of three letters meaning the same as **request**.
9. Write a word of four letters which means **daybreak**.
10. The noun **rapidity** in this extract is formed by adding **ity** to the adjective **rapid.** Form nouns from these adjectives in the same way, then use each in a sentence of your own.
     equal; local; stupid; real; timid.

11. The cargo of meat was **discharged**. The missing words in these sentences all begin with **dis**. Can you find them?

    (a) To –––––– a man is to take his weapons from him.

    (b) When a rider gets down from his horse he is said to ––––––––.

    (c) America was –––––––––– by Christopher Columbus.

    (d) The word ––––––––– means **to go out of sight**.

    (e) When you ––––––––– your shoulder you put it out of joint.

Composition

1. Write an account of the hunting expedition as Ned might have written it in his diary.
2. Describe any feat of magic which Ned might have performed in order to impress the natives.

Exercise 19

Tom Sawyer & Co. Turn Pirates

About midnight Tom arrived with a boiled ham and a few trifles, and stopped in a dense undergrowth on a small bluff overlooking the meeting-place. It was starlight, and very still. The mighty river lay like an ocean at rest. Tom listened a moment but no sound disturbed the quiet. Then he gave a low, distinct whistle. It was answered from under the bluff. Tom whistled twice more; these signals were answered in the same way. Then a guarded voice said:

"Who goes there?"

"Tom Sawyer, the Black Avenger of the Spanish Main. Name your names."

"Huck Finn, the Red-handed, and Joe Harper, the Terror of the Seas."

Tom had furnished these titles from his favourite literature.

" 'Tis well. Give the countersign."

Two hoarse whispers delivered the same awful word simultaneously to the brooding night:

"BLOOD!"

Then Tom tumbled his ham over the bluff and let himself down after it, tearing both skin and clothes to some extent in the effort. There was an easy, comfortable path along the shore under the bluff, but it lacked the advantages of difficulty and danger so valued by a pirate.

(From *The Adventures of Tom Sawyer*, by Mark Twain.)

1. At what time did this incident take place?
2. Was it very dark at the time?

3. How many boys took part in this escapade?
4. How many times was the whistle answered?
5. Where did the answering whistles come from?
6. What title did Tom Sawyer give himself?
7. Do you think the names chosen were suitable for boys who intended becoming pirates?
8. What was the countersign which the boys had agreed upon?
9. What food did Tom Sawyer bring with him?
10. Why did Tom let himself down over the bluff although there was an easy, comfortable path along the shore under the bluff?
11. What damage did he suffer in letting himself down?
12. Write two phrases which show that the river in question was a very wide one.
13. On reaching the meeting-place, what did Tom do before whistling?
14. What kind of books did Tom enjoy reading?

Word Study

1. Write the word in the extract which means **password**.
2. The word **bluff** here means **a steep cliff or bank**. Can you write a sentence using the word in another sense?
3. Write the word in the passage which means **happening at the same time**.
4. Give the opposites of:
   difficulty; midnight; distinct; danger; advantages; comfortable; arrived.
5. Tom stopped in a dense **undergrowth**. Here are twelve words which begin with **under**. Use any of these words to complete the following sentences:
   underfoot   underneath   underclothes

undertone	**underdone**	**underline**
understudy	**understand**	**undergo**
undertaker	**underground**	**underfed**

(a) The meat was tough because it was **under————**.

(b) There were so many things **under————** that we trod on some of them.

(c) Mr. Taylor has to **under——** a serious operation.

(d) An **under———** child is one who does not get enough to eat.

(e) In our English exercise we had to **under————** the nouns in each sentence.

(f) The **under—————** said the coffin was made of oak.

(g) Mollie spoke to her friend in an **under————**.

(h) A submarine can travel **under—————** the water.

(i) When in London we often travel on the **under-——————**.

(j) We could not **under—————** what the Frenchman was saying.

(k) The star was ill, so her **under—————** was called on to take the part.

(l) Many people wear woollen **under———————** in the winter.

Composition

1. Write an account of this incident as Tom Sawyer might have related it to a school chum.

2. Write a short description of a pirate, remembering what you have read in books like *Treasure Island*.

3. Describe briefly what happened when pirates forced their captives to **walk the plank**.

Exercise 20

Attacked by Jackals

Our banquet over, and the sun on the point of retiring to rest, we resolved to follow its example. After prayers we went to our tent, where we found that our housekeeper had provided fresh moss and grass for our beds. Each retired to his separate corner; the little ape, whose protection was undertaken by Frederick and Rudly, nestled in between his two friends, who covered him with moss to protect him from the night cold. I was the last to enter the tent, which I closed behind me, and was soon fast asleep.

I had not been sleeping long when I was disturbed by the barking of our dogs, whom I had posted outside our tent as sentinels. Comprehending that an enemy was near I arose, and my wife and Frederick followed my example; each seized a gun which I had placed within reach, and then we sallied from our habitation, my wife undertaking to keep our guns loaded, for though she carried a musket she doubted the accuracy of her aim.

By the full, clear moonlight we beheld a terrible struggle. A dozen jackals had attacked our two dogs; the latter had already brought to the ground three or four of their antagonists and held the rest of the troop at bay by their bold and rapid movements. They were, however, in danger of being overwhelmed by numbers when we appeared on the scene. A couple of well-directed shots levelled one of the marauders and put the others to flight. Two of the fugitives were pinned by our dogs, slain and devoured. We then returned to our tent; Frederick, who had shot dead one of the jackals, dragging it after him to protect it from the dogs, that he might display the trophy of his victory on the morrow to his brothers.

(Adapted from *The Swiss Family Robinson,* by J. R. Wyss.)

1. At what time of day did the family go to bed?
2. What did they do before entering their tent?
3. What were their beds made of?
4. Who provided the materials for the beds?
5. Where did the little ape sleep?
6. Why was he covered with moss?
7. What did the writer do after entering the tent?
8. What awakened the writer soon after he went to sleep?
9. Why had the dogs been placed outside the tent?
10. How many dogs were there?
11. How many of the family seized guns?
12. Why did the wife not wish to fire her gun?
13. What was her job to be?
14. What had set the dogs barking?
15. Why were the dogs in danger of being overwhelmed?
16. How many jackals were killed by the dogs?
17. Why did Frederick wish to keep the jackal he had shot?
18. Why did he drag it after him?

Word Study

1. Which long word in the passage means **foes**?
2. Frederick shot a jackal dead. What is the dead body of any animal called?
3. Can you give another word beginning with **sen** which means much the same as **sentinel**?
4. What does **habitation** mean?
5. Which word means **animals or persons which go about in search of plunder**?

81

6. Which word means **those who are running away**?
7. Several English words begin with **com**, like **comprehending** in this extract. Can you finish the words beginning with **com** in the following sentences?
   (a) The king **com**—————— the guard to release the prisoner.
   (b) People who take their own lives are said to **com**——— suicide.
   (c) The pirates **com**—————— their captives to walk the plank.
   (d) Harold will **com**———— in four events at the sports.
   (e) I hope you can **com**—————— all these sentences.
   (f) Handel started to **com**————music when he was only a child.
   (g) Mother had to **com**————— to the butcher about the tough meat.
   (h) The concert is due to **com**————— at 7 p.m.
8. What word of three letters means the same as **beheld**?
9. Write a simpler word for **comprehending**.

Composition

1. Write an account of what happened that night as Frederick might have related it to his brothers.
2. Write the conversation which might have taken place between the writer and his wife when they seized their guns.
3. Give an account of any brave deed done by a dog.

Exercise 21

Jack Rogers' Escape

Poor Jack Rogers was dragged along by his savage companions, the muzzle of a pistol or the point of a long knife every now and then being shown him, as a hint that he must keep moving. In one or two openings between giant palms, bananas, and other lofty trees, Jack caught sight of some blue ranges of mountains in the far distance, and towards them, as they pushed their way through the dense undergrowth, his captors seemed to be proceeding. The dreadful thought occurred to him that he was being carried off into the interior to be turned into a slave. Suddenly there was a rustling of leaves, a crashing of boughs. A loud shriek was uttered, and a huge animal leaped through the brushwood, and, seizing one of the Negroes, bounded off into the thicket. The unfortunate wretch cried out piteously for help. The Spaniards and the Negroes turned to pursue the wild beast, and were soon hidden from Jack's sight by the trees. He had no wish to follow them even had he possessed the power to do so. His arms were bound, and before he could do anything he must contrive to get them loose. He tugged and tugged frantically.

At last he twisted the rope round so that he could reach one of the knots with his teeth. He pulled away lustily, and found that he was slackening it. One more tug and his hands were at liberty, and after a moment's reflection he determined to find his way as soon as possible to the banks of the river, for he was certain that boats would be sent in to look for his party, and by watching for them, he hoped to be able to make some signal to call their attention to himself.

(Adapted from *The Three Midshipmen*, by W. H. G. Kingston.)

1. Name two things which were used to keep Jack moving.
2. Where did Jack's captors appear to be making for?
3. What was Jack's great fear as they moved along?
4. What noises were caused by the animal?
5. Whom did the animal attack?
6. What did the rest of the party do after the attack?
7. Why did they so soon disappear from Jack's sight?
8. Give two reasons why Jack did not follow them.
9. In what way did Jack take advantage of his captors' absence?
10. Why did he twist the rope round that bound his arms?
11. Where did Jack intend making for after getting his hands free?
12. Why did he decide to go in this direction?
13. How did he intend to call attention to himself?
14. This incident took place in Africa. What is there in the extract to show that it did not happen in Britain?

Word Study

1. **Captors** are people who capture others. What are the people who are captured called?
2. Write the opposite of **interior**.
3. **Spaniards** are natives of **Spain**. What are the natives of these countries called:
   (a) Norway;
   (b) Sweden;
   (c) Finland;
   (d) Portugal;
   (e) Switzerland?

4. **Slacken** means **to make slack**. Give one word, ending in **en**, for each of the following:
   (a) to make longer;
   (b) to make stronger;
   (c) to make wider;
   (d) to make smarter;
   (e) to make glad.
5. The word **wretch** has a silent **w**; so have the words indicated below. Do you know them?
   (a) a ring of flowers or leaves twisted together
   (b) very great anger
   (c) to move by turning or twisting, as a worm does
   (d) to try to throw an opponent to the ground
   (e) the joint between your hand and your arm
6. The plural of **Negro** is **Negroes**. Write the plurals of these words ending with **o**, some of which add **es**, others just **s**:
   (a) tomato;   (d) potato;
   (b) solo;   (e) hero;
   (c) piano;   (f) cargo.
7. There was a **rustling** of leaves; a **crashing** of boughs. What words are used to denote the following sounds:
   (a) a door with rusty hinges being opened or closed;
   (b) the brakes of a car being applied in pulling up quickly;
   (c) dry wood burning in a blazing fire;
   (d) raindrops beating against a window;
   (e) church bells being rung at a wedding?

Composition

1. Many famous books contain accounts of escapes. Write an account of an imaginary escape in which you are the central figure.

2. Write an account of this incident as it might have been related by Jack Rogers.
3. Human beings are often attacked by wild beasts. Imagine that you witnessed the attack described in this extract. Write a letter to your parents telling them of your experience.

Exercise 22

Grace Darling to the Rescue

Grace Darling, the daughter of the keeper of one of the lighthouses upon the Farne Islands, a perilous cluster of rocks off Northumberland, was awakened towards the morning of the 6th September, 1838, by shrieks of distress; and when dawn came, perceived the remains of a wreck on Longstone Island, the outermost of the group.

She awoke her father and urged him to launch his boat and go to the rescue of anyone who might still be alive in the stranded vessel, but the tide was rising, wind and sea were wild, and the old man hung back. Grace, however, was sure she discerned a movement on the wreck, as though living beings were still there, and seizing an oar, placed herself in the boat, which she was well able to manage. Her father could not let her go alone, and they rowed off together in a tremendous sea, encouraged by perceiving that nine persons were still clinging to the forepart of the ship. The father, after many vain attempts, succeeded in landing on the rock and making his way to the wreck, while Grace rowed off and on among the breakers, skilfully guiding her little boat, which but for her excellent management would have been dashed to pieces against the rocks.

One by one the nine survivors were placed in the boat and carried to the lighthouse, where Grace fed, lodged and nursed them for two whole days before the storm abated enough for communication with the mainland. One of them was a Mrs. Dawson, whose two children, eleven and eight years old, had actually been buffeted to death by the waves while she held them in her arms, and who was so much injured herself that it was long before she could leave her bed.

(From *A Book of Golden Deeds*, by Charlotte M. Yonge.)

1. Where are the Farne Islands?
2. Why did Grace awaken so early that morning?
3. What did she see when day dawned?
4. What did she want her father to do?
5. Why did her father hesitate to do as she wished?
6. What made Grace all the more determined to go to the rescue?
7. Why did Grace's father go with her after all?
8. What encouraged them during their dangerous errand?
9. What was the name of the island on which they landed?
10. How do you know that there was great difficulty in landing?
11. What did the father do when he reached the rock?
12. What did Grace do? Why?
13. How many people were rescued?
14. How long did they stay in the lighthouse before being taken ashore?
15. How many years ago did this happen?

Word Study

1. The words **lighthouse** and **mainland** are compound words, being made up of two smaller words. Can you pair the words in columns **A** and **B** opposite, so as to form other well-known compound words?

88

Column A	Column B
break	master
sun	box
black	flake
bed	seller
snow	water
head	side
match	smith
book	shine

2. The prefix **dis** in **discern** is found in several words in English. Write the following sentences, completing each word which begins with **dis**.
   (a) The noise of the traffic **dis** — — — — — the children's rest.
   (b) Hundreds of toys were **dis** — — — — — in the shop window.
   (c) The shop assistant was **dis** — — — — — for stealing.
   (d) The detective **dis** — — — — — himself as a gypsy.
   (e) Dandelion seeds are **dis** — — — — — by the wind.

3. Write a common word which means the same as **perilous**.

4. The **forepart** of a ship means the **front part**. Write the words beginning with **fore** which fit these meanings:
   (a) the front paws of a dog;
   (b) to tell what the future holds;
   (c) the front mast in a ship with more than one mast;
   (d) the part of your arm between wrist and elbow;
   (e) a tennis stroke in which the hand is turned to the front.

Composition

1. Write an account of the rescue of the shipwrecked people as it might have been told:
   (a) by Grace Darling;

    (b) by her father;

    (c) by one of the survivors.

2. Imagine that after the storm you were taken ashore. Write a letter to Grace Darling praising her bravery and expressing your gratitude.

Exercise 23

The Headless Horseman

The dominant spirit that haunts the enchanted region of Sleepy Hollow is the apparition of a figure on horseback without a head. It is said by some to be the ghost of a Hessian trooper, whose head had been carried away by a cannon ball, and who is frequently seen hurrying along in the gloom of night, as if on the wings of the wind. His haunts are not confined to the valley, but extend at times to the adjacent roads, and especially to the vicinity of a nearby church.

Indeed, local historians who have been collecting facts concerning this spectre allege that, the body of the trooper, having been buried in the churchyard, the ghost rides forth to the scene of the battle in nightly quest of his head; and that the rushing speed with which he sometimes passes along the hollow, like a midnight blast, is owing to his being belated, and in a hurry to get back to the churchyard before daybreak.

This superstition has furnished materials for many a wild story in that region of shadows; and the spectre is known at all the country firesides by the name of The Headless Horseman of Sleepy Hollow.

(From *The Legend of Sleepy Hollow*, by Washington Irving.)

1. This region was haunted by several ghosts. Which was the chief?
2. How did the Hessian trooper lose his life?
3. Where was the body of the Hessian trooper buried?

4. Why did his body ride abroad at night?
5. Write the phrases which show that the ghost's horse travelled at a terrific speed.
6. Why was the ghost in such a hurry?
7. What was the full name which the people of the district gave to the ghost?
8. From where did the ghost start his nightly ride?
9. Write two phrases which the author uses to describe Sleepy Hollow. The word **region** appears in both.

Word Study

1. Write **three** words which mean the same as **ghost**.
2. **Churchyard** is a compound word made up of **church** and **yard**. What are the following **yards** called?
   (a) The **yard** which surrounds a farm house.
   (b) A **yard** in which are the graves of many dead.
   (c) A **yard** in which bricks are made.
   (d) A **yard** where ships are built, repaired and fitted out.
   (e) The **yard** at the back of a house.
3. Use your dictionary to find the exact meaning of each of these words, then use them in sentences of your own:
   dominant; confined; adjacent; vicinity; superstition; furnished.
4. Form a noun from the verb **enchant**.
5. The word **fireside** is a compound word. Can you find these words beginning with **fire**? Use your dictionary, if necessary.
   (a) Revolvers, rifles and other shooting weapons are called **fire** ————.
   (b) On November 5th thousands of **fire** ————— are let off in Britain.

(c) The daring **fire**——— rescued the children from the blazing building.

(d) The **fire**——— is an insect which gives out light when it flies at night.

(e) George chopped a pile of **fire**———— for his mother.

(f) In the huge open **fire**————— a log fire was burning brightly.

(g) So brightly did it burn that we could read by the **fire**—————.

(h) A **fire**————— material is one which, like the safety curtain in a theatre, will not burn.

6. Write a word of four letters which means the same as **daybreak**.

7. The ghost went **nightly** in quest of his head. What words ending with **ly** are used for these phrases:

(a) every twenty-four hours;

(b) every seven days;

(c) every twenty-eight days;

(d) every three months;

(e) every twelve months?

8. The Headless Horseman was **belated**, that is, delayed or made late. The word **belate** is formed by placing **be** before **late**. Write the following sentences, completing the words which begin with **be**.

(a) Charles I was **be**—————— in Whitehall in 1649.

(b) The wind dropped and the sailing ship was **be-** ——————.

(c) The city of Jericho was **be**—————— by Joshua's army. Nobody could enter, nobody could leave.

(d) The man was so mean that he **be**——————— his children new clothes.

(e) The word **be**———— means "to be on guard against something", *e.g.*, **be**———— of the dog.

93

(f) Our fingers were **be**———— by the intense cold.

(g) A kind policeman **be**———— the lost children.

Composition

1. Imagine that you lived in Sleepy Hollow, and that one night you saw the Headless Horseman. Describe what you saw.

2. Write an imaginary account of an incident which took place in a haunted house.

Exercise 24

The Death of Samson

The lords of the Philistines sent word to the keeper of the prison house that Samson should be brought into the temple, and the tumult died down to a profound hush. But when, shuffling and groping, Samson was led in by the lad who was in charge of him, and appeared in the midst of the temple, a wild, prolonged yell of hate and triumph went up from the throats of all assembled there. The walls trembled at the sound of it, and Samson, mighty even in ruin, goaded on like a beast with whip and cry, was compelled to make sport for them all until they were weary.

At length, even the most pitiless of his persecutors were sated of it, and Samson turned to the lad at his side and asked him to lead him a little nearer to the two central columns which held up the roof. The lad did as Samson asked of him. The people had ceased to watch him, for the priests of Dagon were now at their frenzied dancing again, to the sound of cymbal and drum. Then Samson prayed: "O, Lord, give me back my strength again this once, that I may take vengeance once on these Philistines for the loss of both mine eyes."

Then he laid hold of the columns, bowed himself, and with all his strength thrust against them, and the walls and roof of the great temple of the Fish God lurched inwards and outwards, and descended on his image, upon his priests, upon his people assembled there, and upon Samson himself.

1. By whom had Samson been imprisoned?
2. What order was given to the keeper of the prison house?

95

3. Who was in charge of Samson?
4. What two things were used to drive Samson along?
5. When did the tumult in the temple die down?
6. When did the people in the temple make the walls tremble with their shouting?
7. What was the name of the god of the Philistines?
8. What was his image like?
9. What did Samson ask the lad to do?
10. What did the people do after they had ceased watching Samson?
11. Why did Samson seek vengeance on the Philistines?
12. What did Samson do after laying hold of the two central columns?
13. This extract tells us that Samson had lost two things. What were they?
14. Why was a lad strong enough to take care of Samson?

Word Study

1. Form nouns from:
   assembled; prayed; descended.
2. Form adjectives from:
   tumult; hate; triumph; watch; might.
3. Write the words in this extract which mean:
   (a) **an uproar;**
   (b) **gathered;**
   (c) **pushed with force;**
   (d) **very excited, almost mad;**
   (e) **stopped;**
   (f) **fully satisfied.**
4. What two musical instruments are mentioned in this extract?

5. Write another word beginning with **i** which means much the same as **image**.
6. The words **central, cymbal, cease,** all begin with the letter **c** which is sounded as **s**. Can you find these words which begin in the same way:
   (a) a drink made from the juice of apples;
   (b) very famous;
   (c) a place for burying the dead;
   (d) wheat, oats, barley, etc.;
   (e) wood or coal partly burned and no longer alight;
   (f) a hundred runs in cricket, or a hundred years;
   (g) any person who is not in the armed forces;
   (h) a tank for storing water?
7. The hush was **profound**; the yell was **prolonged**. Write these other words which begin with **pro**.
   (a) The children found it hard to **pro**−−−−−− the word.
   (b) Nets were used to **pro**−−−− the fruit trees from birds.
   (c) The players **pro**−−−−−− against the referee's decision.
   (d) In 1939 war was **pro**−−−−−−− against Germany.
   (e) Britain cannot **pro**−−−− enough wheat for her people.
   (f) The constable was **pro**−−−−− to the rank of sergeant.

Composition

1. There are many stories of Samson's immense strength. Read one of these stories in the Bible, then write it in your own words.
2. Write an account of the Death of Samson as you would tell it to a very young child.

97

Exercise 25

The Gorgons

The three Gorgons bore some distant resemblance to women, but were really a frightful species of dragon. Instead of hair they had each of them a hundred enormous snakes growing on their heads, all alive, twisting, wriggling, curling and thrusting out their venomous tongues with forked stings at the end. The teeth of the Gorgons were terribly long tusks; their hands were made of brass; their bodies were covered with hard, impenetrable scales. They had wings, too, every feather in which was pure glittering gold, and they looked very dazzling when the Gorgons were flying about in the sunshine.

But when people caught a glimpse of their glittering brightness aloft in the air, they seldom stopped to gaze, but ran and hid themselves as speedily as they could. You will think, perhaps, that they were afraid of being stung by the serpents, or of having their heads bitten off by the long tusks, or of being torn to pieces by the brazen claws. But the worst thing about these abominable Gorgons was that, if once a poor mortal fixed his eyes full upon one of their faces he was certain that very instant to be changed from warm flesh and blood into cold and lifeless stone.

(From *The Wonder Book,* by Nathaniel Hawthorne.)

1. Were the Gorgons women?
2. Describe what grew on the Gorgons' heads in place of hair.
3. What were the Gorgons' teeth like?

4. What was extraordinary about the Gorgons' wings?
5. What did people do when they caught a glimpse of the brightness in the air which heralded the coming of the Gorgons?
6. Name the four things of which the people were afraid.
7. Which was the greatest of these dangers?
8. What happened to a person who was a victim of this greatest danger?
9. What were the claws of the Gorgons made of?

Word Study

1. Write the word which means **poisonous**.
2. Which word in the passage means **hateful**?
3. The word **impenetrable** means **cannot be penetrated**, or **cannot be pierced**. What adjectives beginning with **im** and ending with **able** would you use to describe:
    (a) an object which is so heavy or which is fixed so firmly that it cannot be **moved**;
    (b) a road which is so thickly covered with snow that nobody can **pass** along it;
    (c) a scheme which cannot be put into **practice**?
4. The Gorgons had long tusks. Can you name any other animals besides the elephant which have tusks?
5. A **tusk** is a long pointed tooth which sticks out of an animal's mouth, a characteristic of the elephant. What animals are indicated by the characteristic parts mentioned in the following sentences?
    (a) After several days without food the hump of the ––––– had become much smaller.
    (b) The –––––––– has a pouch in front in which it carries its young ones.

99

(c) The tail of a – – – is called the **brush**.

(d) The – – – – – – is a sea creature which has eight tentacles.

(e) The branching horns of a – – – – are called antlers.

6. Write the opposites of:

   mortal; difficult; seldom; greatest; pure.

7. Write a word of four letters beginning with **h** which means much the same as **enormous**.

8. Which word in the passage means **a person who is sure to die sometime**?

9. The Gorgons' wings were glittering and dazzling. Look carefully at the adjectives given below and use them to fill the blanks in the sentences which follow:

   twinkling; dazzling; shining; glistening; sparkling.

   (a) Although it was early morning the sun was – – – – – – brightly.

   (b) A powerful car swung round the corner of the dark street, its headlights – – – – – – – our eyes.

   (c) Looking upwards we saw millions of stars – – – – – – – – in the heavens.

   (d) The diamonds were – – – – – – – – under the lights in the jeweller's shop window.

   (e) In the morning sunshine we saw countless dewdrops – – – – – – – – – on trees and hedges.

10. The serpents were **wriggling**. Can you find the missing words below, each of which begins with a silent **w**?

    (a) The ship was sent on to the rocks by the storm and soon became a **w** – – – –.

    (b) The old gipsy's face had many a **w** – – – – – –.

    (c) I helped mother to **w** – – – – the water from the clothes.

    (d) The **w** – – – is one of the smallest birds in the British Isles.

    (e) The books were **w** – – – – – – in strong brown paper.

100

Composition

1. Write a brief description of a Gorgon, using your own words as far as possible.
2. Suppose that you had been given the power to look a Gorgon full in the face without suffering any harm. Describe what happened to a person you saw looking upon the face of one of these monsters.

Exercise 26

Catching Wild Goats

Being now in the eleventh year of my residence on the island and my ammunition growing low, I planned to trap and snare the goats, to see whether I could not catch some of them alive. So I made snares to hamper them, and they were more than once taken in them; but my tackle was not good, for I had no wire, and I always found them broken and my bait devoured.

At length I resolved to try a pitfall, so I dug several large pits in the earth, in places where the goats used to feed; and over these pits I placed hurdles with a great weight upon them. Several times I put ears of barley, and dry rice, without setting the trap; and I could easily perceive that the goats had gone in and eaten up the corn, for I could see the marks of their feet.

At length I set three traps in one night, and next morning I found them all standing, and yet the bait had gone. This was very discouraging. However, I altered my trap, and one morning I found in one of them an old he-goat, and in another three kids—a male and two females.

The old one was so fierce that I dare not go near him to bring him away alive. I could have killed him, but that was not my business. So I let him out, and he ran away as if he had been frightened out of his wits. I did not know then what I learnt afterwards—that hunger will tame a lion. If I had left him there three or four days without food, and carried him some water to drink, and then a little corn, he would have been as tame as one of the kids. Then I went to the three kids, and taking them one by one I tied them with strings together, and with some difficulty brought them all home.

(Adapted from *Robinson Crusoe*, by Daniel Defoe.)

1. How long had Crusoe been living on the island when this incident took place?
2. Why did Crusoe wish to catch the goats alive?
3. Why were the goats able to get out of the snares?
4. How did Crusoe plan to trap the goats after the snares had failed?
5. How did Crusoe know that the goats had gone in and eaten the corn?
6. How many goats in all were caught after the trap had been altered?
7. Why was Crusoe afraid to go into the pit where the old he-goat was?
8. What did the old goat do when Crusoe let him out?
9. How could Crusoe have tamed the old goat?
10. Why did he not do this?
11. What did Crusoe do with the kids?
12. What did he do to prevent them escaping during the journey home?

Word Study

1. The adjective **eleventh** has been formed from the word **eleven.** Form adjectives from:
   one; two; three; four; five; nine.
2. A **kid** is a young goat. What are the following called:
   (a) a young cow;

103

    (b) a young wolf;

    (c) a young sheep;

    (d) a young horse;

    (e) a young eagle?

3. Write **one** word for **marks of the feet**.

4. Write a word of **three** letters which means **devoured**.

5. Crusoe used a **pitfall**. Complete these sentences with **fall** in each case.

    (a) The ————**fall** of the cruel ruler was greeted with joy.

    (b) A ————**fall** is an unexpected piece of good fortune.

    (c) Niagara is the best known —————**fall** in the world.

    (d) The heavy ————**fall** covered the earth with a white mantle.

    (e) Streams of water swept down the hilly streets of Ayford during yesterday's heavy ————**fall**.

6. There were two female kids and one male.

    (a) What is a male goat usually called?

    (b) What is a female goat usually called?

7. The snares were **broken**, the bait was **eaten**. These words are the participles of the verbs **break** and **eat**. Write the following sentences using the correct participle of the verb at the end.

    (a) Michael's face was ——————— as the result of tooth-ache. **(swell)**

    (b) The treasure was —————— in a large cave. **(hide)**

    (c) Four people were ——————— in the boating accident. **(drown)**

    (d) The bell was ———— at four o'clock. **(ring)**

    (e) Three players were ———— in the football match. **(hurt)**

8. Write a word of **six** letters beginning with **sc** which means the same as frightened.

Composition

1. Write a short composition suggesting some uses to which Crusoe put the skins of the goats after they had been killed.
2. Write three daily entries as you think they would appear in a diary kept by Robinson Crusoe, giving brief accounts of his attempts to trap wild goats.

Exercise 27

King Richard and the Nubian Slave

King Richard read and mused in the entrance of his pavilion; behind, with his back to the entrance, the Nubian slave burnished the big shield. In front of all, a hundred paces distant, the yeomen of the guard stood, sat or lay on the grass, while betwixt them and the front of the tent lay the senseless form of the little old Turk, dressed like a marabout or monk.

But the Nubian had the advantage of a mirror, the highly polished shield, in which he beheld the marabout raise his head gently from the ground so as to survey all around him. Satisfied that he was unobserved he began to drag himself nearer and nearer to the king, till he was about ten yards from Richard's person, when, starting on his feet, he sprang forward and stood at the king's back brandishing aloft a dagger which he had hidden in his sleeve.

The whole of the army could not have saved their heroic monarch, but ere the marabout could strike, the Nubian caught his uplifted arm. Turning his fanatical wrath upon the slave the marabout dealt him a blow with the dagger which, however, only grazed his arm, while the far superior strength of the Nubian easily dashed him to the ground.

Seeing what had happened Richard jumped up, seized the stool on which he had been sitting and dashed almost to pieces the skull of the assassin, who expired at the king's feet. Then, turning to the Nubian, he said, "Thou art wounded, and with a poisoned weapon, I warrant. Suck the poison from his wound, one of you;" he commanded, seeing that the yeomen had now arrived on the scene, "the venom is harmless on the lips, though fatal when it mingles with the blood."

The yeomen looked at each other with hesitation.

"How now?" said the king, "Do you fear death that you dally thus? I never bade man do that which I would not do myself." And without delay the King of England applied his lips to the wound of the black slave.

(Adapted from *The Talisman*, by Sir Walter Scott.)

1. Where was the king seated?
2. On what was he seated?
3. Where was the Nubian slave?
4. What was he doing?
5. Name the three positions in which the yeomen of the guard were:
   (a) –––––**ing**   (b) ––––**ing**   (c) ––**ing.**
6. Who lay on the ground between the king and his yeomen?
7. How far from the king were the yeomen?
8. What served the slave as a mirror?
9. What did he see in this mirror?
10. What was the marabout trying to do?
11. What happened when he came within ten yards of the king?
12. Who saved the king's life?
13. How do you know that the Nubian was much stronger than the marabout?
14. How, and by whom, was the marabout killed?
15. What treatment did the king prescribe for the Nubian?
16. Why had he to give this treatment himself?

Word Study

1. Write the words in this extract which mean:
   - (a) **between;**
   - (b) **king;**
   - (c) **died;**
   - (d) **mixes;**
   - (e) **poison;**
   - (f) **delay.**

2. Three words in this passage end with **ished**. Complete the following sentences by using words which end in the same way.
   - (a) The word ———**ished** means disappeared.
   - (b) Slavery was ————**ished** in America in 1865.
   - (c) When a person is —————**ished** he is greatly surprised.
   - (d) The plants ————— **ished** because they had good soil, rain and sunshine.
   - (e) When we say that the lights were ———————**ished** we mean that they were put out.

3. Write a sentence using the word **grazed** in a different sense from that given in the extract.

4. The marabout was a **fanatic** and an **assassin**. What are these people called:
   - (a) one who suffers death or torture because of his religion;
   - (b) one who goes on a journey to a holy place;
   - (c) one who listens at keyholes and other places in order to hear talk that he is not supposed to hear;
   - (d) a person who is unable to pay his debts;
   - (e) a person who asks awkward questions at a meeting in order to annoy a speaker?

5. What are these four words which begin with the same three letters as **assassin**:
   - (a) help;
   - (b) mixed;
   - (c) gathered together;
   - (d) taken for granted?

6. Form adjectives from:

   advantage; wrath; poison; venom; ridicule.

7. A **Turk** is a native of **Turkey**. What are the natives of these countries called:
   - (a) Wales;
   - (b) Scotland;
   - (c) Ireland;
   - (d) Isle of Man;
   - (e) Malta?

Composition

1. Write a short account of this incident as the slave might have related it to the king.
2. Imagine that you are King Richard. Say how you would reward the Nubian for saving your life.

Exercise 28

Oliver Twist Asks for More

The room in the workhouse in which the boys were fed was a large stone hall, with a copper at one end; out of which the master, assisted by one or two women, ladled the gruel at meal-times. Each boy had one porringer, and no more—except on occasions of great public rejoicing, when he had two ounces and a quarter of bread besides. The bowls never wanted washing. The boys polished them with their spoons until they shone again.

Oliver Twist and his companions suffered the tortures of slow starvation for three months. At last they got so voracious and wild with hunger that a council was held; lots were cast who should walk up to the master after supper that evening and ask for more; and it fell to Oliver Twist.

The evening arrived, the boys took their places; the master stationed himself at the copper with his pauper assistants ranged behind him; the gruel was served out and soon disappeared. The boys whispered to each other and winked at Oliver, while his neighbours nudged him. Child as he was, he was desperate with hunger and reckless with misery. He rose, and advancing to the master, basin and spoon in hand, said, "Please, sir, I want some more."

The master turned pale, and gazed in stupefied astonishment on the small rebel for some seconds; then clung for support to the copper. The assistants were paralysed with wonder, the boys with fear.

"What!" said the master at length, in a faint voice.

"Please, sir," replied Oliver, "I want some more."

The master aimed a blow at Oliver's head with the ladle, pinioned him in his arms, and shrieked aloud for Mr. Bumble, the beadle.

(Adapted from *Oliver Twist*, by Charles Dickens.)

1. Where were the boys fed?
2. Who fed them?
3. What extra food did they get on special occasions?
4. Why did their bowls never need washing?
5. Why did the boys hold a council one day?
6. What was decided at that council?
7. Why did Oliver's neighbours nudge him on the appointed evening?
8. What did Oliver do after being nudged?
9. Which two phrases describe how Oliver felt that evening?
10. What effect did Oliver's request have on the master?
11. What effect did it have on the assistants?
12. What effect did it have on the boys?
13. Name three things which the master did when Oliver repeated his request.
14. Oliver's neighbours nudged him. Name two things which the other boys did.

Word Study

1. Write simpler words for:
   assisted; voracious; council.
2. Use the following words (a) as *nouns* and (b) as *verbs*:
   master; rebel; washing; support; wonder.
3. Which word in this passage shows that the master's assistants were very, very poor?

4. What is a **porringer**?
5. What were the people who lived in workhouses called?
6. What are the following people called:
    (a) people receiving medical treatment;
    (b) people buying goods in a shop;
    (c) people who consult a solicitor;
    (d) people travelling by train, bus, ship, etc.?
7. This extract contains the names of various things used in connection with meals:

    basin; spoon; ladle; porringer.

    Can you name the following articles which are used in the same way:
    (a) a deep, covered dish from which soups and vegetables are served;
    (b) a machine which cuts meat into small pieces;
    (c) a stand with bottles in which salt, pepper and vinegar are kept;
    (d) a small tin or box in which the tea is kept;
    (e) a dish with small holes which is used for straining cabbage and other vegetables?
8. A **pauper** is a very poor person who is dependent on charity. What are these persons called:
    (a) a person who lives very poorly in order to hoard money;
    (b) a person who spends money recklessly;
    (c) one who eats more than is good for him;
    (d) a person who betrays his country, friend, etc.;
    (e) one who offers his services of his own free will?

Composition

1. Write an imaginary conversation that might have taken place among the boys at the council they held.

2. Write an account of this incident as one of the boys might have told it to another boy who was not present.
3. Write a short composition entitled:
   Why I Asked For More—by Oliver Twist.

Exercise 29

Rikki-tikki-tavi

He was a mongoose, rather like a little cat in his fur and tail, but quite like a weasel in his head and his habits. His eyes and the end of his restless nose were pink; he could scratch himself anywhere he pleased; with any leg, front or back, that he chose to use; he could fluff up his tail till it looked like a bottle-brush, and his war-cry, as he scuttled through the long grass, was: "Rikk-tikk-tikki-tikki-tchk!"

One day, a high summer flood washed him out of the burrow where he lived with his father and mother, and carried him, kicking and clucking, down a roadside ditch. He found a little wisp of grass floating there, and clung to it till he lost his senses. When he revived, he was lying in the hot sun on the middle of a garden path, very draggled indeed, and a small boy was saying "Here's a dead mongoose. Let's have a funeral."

"No," said his mother; "let's take him in and dry him. Perhaps he isn't really dead."

They took him into the house, and a big man picked him up between his finger and thumb, and said he was not dead but half choked; so they wrapped him in cotton-wool, and warmed him, and he opened his eyes and sneezed.

"Now," said the big man (he was an Englishman who had just moved into the bungalow), "don't frighten him, and we'll see what he'll do."

It is the hardest thing in the world to frighten a mongoose, because he is eaten up from nose to tail with curiosity.

(From *The Jungle Book,* by Rudyard Kipling. By kind permission of Mrs. George Bambridge, daughter of the late Rudyard Kipling, and by courtesy of the publishers, Macmillan & Co. Ltd.)

1. Name two ways in which Rikki resembled a little cat.
2. In what way was he like a weasel?
3. Where did Rikki live?
4. Explain how Rikki was carried down a roadside ditch.
5. What did Rikki do just before he lost his senses?
6. Where did he find himself when he recovered?
7. Who found him there?
8. In what condition was he when found?
9. What did the finder want to do with Rikki?
10. What did the woman suggest doing with him?
11. What did the big man say was the matter with Rikki?
12. Name two things which were done to revive him.
13. Name two things which Rikki did when he came round again.
14. Why is it hard to frighten a mongoose?

Word Study

1. Write the plural of **mongoose**.
2. The word **bottle-brush** is made up of the two words **bottle** and **brush**. Write three other words, the second part of which is **brush**.
3. Rikki lived in a **burrow**. Rabbits also live in burrows. Complete these sentences by using the names of the animals' homes.
   (a) The lion returned to his — — — with a young goat.
   (b) The beavers were busy building their — — — — —.
   (c) Ben keeps eight tame rabbits in large — — — — —.
   (d) The doves flew down and alighted on the roof of their — — — —.
   (e) When hunted by the hounds the fox sought refuge in its — — — — —.

4. Rikki clung to a wisp of grass; that is, a small piece of grass. Here are five words, each meaning a small piece. Can you fit them into the phrases which follow?

splinter; speck; crumb; morsel; grain.

(a) a ───── of bread or cake

(b) a ───── of sand

(c) a ───── of dirt

(d) a ──────── of wood

(e) a ───── of food

5. Rikki **scuttled** through the long grass. Complete these sentences by using the verb in the list below which best describes the action of the creatures.

scampered	prowled
wallowed	lumbered
gnawed	swooped
soared	pounced

(a) All night the lions ──────── round the camp.

(b) The eagle ──────── down on its prey.

(c) The rabbits ───── the trunks of the trees.

(d) The elephants ──────── in the muddy stream.

(e) Suddenly a skylark ───── into the sky.

(f) The brown bear ──────── through the woods.

(g) The frightened mouse ───────── back to its hole.

(h) The cat ──────── on the mouse as it was leaving its hole.

Composition

1. From what you have read in this passage write a short description of a mongoose.

2. Write an account of this incident as Rikki might have told it to his mother and father.

Exercise 30

The End of Carver Doone

I stretched forth my left hand to let him have the hug of me, but in this I was too generous; having forgotten my pistol-wound and the cracking of one of my short lower ribs. Carver Doone caught me round the waist with such a grip as never yet had been laid on me.

I heard my rib go; I grasped his arm, and tore the muscle out of it as the string comes out of an orange; then I took him by the throat, which is not allowed in wrestling; but he had snatched at mine. In vain he tugged, and strained, and writhed, dashed his bleeding fist into my face, and flung himself on me with gnashing jaws. Beneath the iron of my strength I had him helpless in two minutes.

"I will not harm thee any more," I cried. "Carver Doone, thou art beaten; own it, and thank God for it; and go thy way and repent."

It was all too late. Even if he would have owned that for the first time in his life he had found his master, it was too late. The black bog had him by the feet; the sucking of the ground drew him on, like the thirsty lips of death. In our fury we had heeded neither wet nor dry, nor thought of the earth beneath us. I myself might scarcely leap, with the last spring of overlaboured legs, from the engulfing grave of slime.

He fell back, and then he tossed his arms to heaven, and they were black to the elbow, and the glare of his eyes was ghastly. I could only gaze and pant, for my strength was no more than an infant's from the fury and the horror. Scarcely could I turn away, while, joint by joint, he sank from sight.

(Adapted from *Lorna Doone*, by R. D. Blackmore.)

1. Why was the writer of this story, John Ridd, too generous in allowing Carver Doone to "have the hug" of him?
2. Where did Carver seize hold of the writer?
3. What effect did this have on John Ridd?
4. How did John Ridd retaliate?
5. Why did John Ridd take his opponent by the throat, although it was not allowed in wrestling?
6. Write the five verbs used to describe Carver Doone's efforts to escape from the writer's grasp.
7. How long did this terrific struggle last?
8. How do you know that Carver Doone had never before been beaten in a fight?
9. Why was it too late for Carver Doone to admit that he was beaten?
10. Name two things which caused John Ridd to become as weak as an infant.

Word Study

1. The word **gnashing** begins with a silent **g**. What words beginning in the same way are indicated below?
   (a) The bark of the young trees has been **gn**———— by rabbits.
   (b) A **gn**—— is a very tiny insect whose bite causes itching.
   (c) A **gn**——— is a dwarf who is supposed to live down inside the earth.
   (d) A **gn**————— tree is one covered with hard rough lumps.
2. Write words which are pronounced exactly like the

118

following words but which are spelt differently:

forth; waist; allowed; heard; vain; time; site; muscle.

3. The following words from the extract are the *past tense* of common verbs. Write the *present tense* of each:

   caught; flung; took; tore; found; drew; thought; sank.

4. Which word of three letters in this passage means:

   the engulfing grave of slime?

5. John Ridd's legs were **overlaboured**. Write these sentences, completing the word beginning with **over** in each.

   (a) The car was fast enough to **over**———— any vehicle on the road.

   (b) The house was so **over**———————— that seven people slept in one room.

   (c) The River Nile **over**————— its banks every year.

   (d) Two of the firemen who entered the burning building were **over**———— by the intense heat.

   (e) I **over**————— father telling mother that he had bought me a bat for my birthday.

   (f) The headmaster said that he would **over**————— my offence this time.

   (g) The rebels **over**————— the government and seized control of the country.

   (h) Children who **over**——— are often sick.

   (i) The plane was so long **over**——— that it was considered lost.

   (j) The slates on a roof always **over**——— one another.

   (k) The woman died from an **over**————— of drugs.

Composition

1. Suppose that you were a witness of this struggle. Write as descriptive an account of it as you can.

2. Dozens of thrilling fights are described in well-known books, *e.g.*

Tom Brown's fight with Slogger Williams;

Martin Rattler's fight with Bob Croaker;

John Ridd's fight with Robin Snell, etc., etc.

Write an account in your own words of any fight you have read about.